MODERN Folk-Rock GUITAR

Project Manager: COLGAN BRYAN
Cover Photo of MAGDA HILLER by MICHELLE SAS
Art Design: LISA GREENE MANE

WARNER BROS. PUBLICATIONS - THE GLOBAL LEADER IN PRINT
USA: 15800 NW 48th Avenue, Miami, FL 33014

WARNER/CHAPPELL MUSIC	NUOVA CARISCH	INTERNATIONAL MUSIC PUBLICATIONS LIMITED
CANADA: 85 SCARSDALE ROAD, SUITE 101	**ITALY:** VIA CAMPANIA, 12	**ENGLAND:** SOUTHEND ROAD,
DON MILLS, ONTARIO, M3B 2R2	20098 S. GIULIANO MILANESE (MI)	WOODFORD GREEN, ESSEX IG8 8HN
SCANDINAVIA: P.O. BOX 533, VENDEVAGEN 85 B	ZONA INDUSTRIALE SESTO ULTERIANO	**GERMANY:** MARSTALLSTR. 8, D-80539 MUNCHEN
S-182 15, DANDERYD, SWEDEN	**SPAIN:** MAGALLANES, 25	**DENMARK:** DANMUSIK, VOGNMAGERGADE 7
AUSTRALIA: P.O. BOX 353	28015 MADRID	DK 1120 KOBENHAVNK
3 TALAVERA ROAD, NORTH RYDE N.S.W. 2113	**FRANCE:** 25 RUE DE HAUTEVILLE, 75010 PARIS	

CONTENTS:

ARTIST INDEX:

THE ACTION

Words and Music by
KEVIN MOORE

Gtrs. in "open D" tuning:

⑥ = D   ③ = F♯
⑤ = A   ② = A
④ = D   ① = D

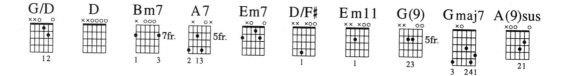

Moderately ♩ = 92

Intro:

Gtr. 1 *(Dobro)*

Verses:

1. Re - mem - ber when we first met?
2. *See additional lyrics*

The Action - 8 - 1

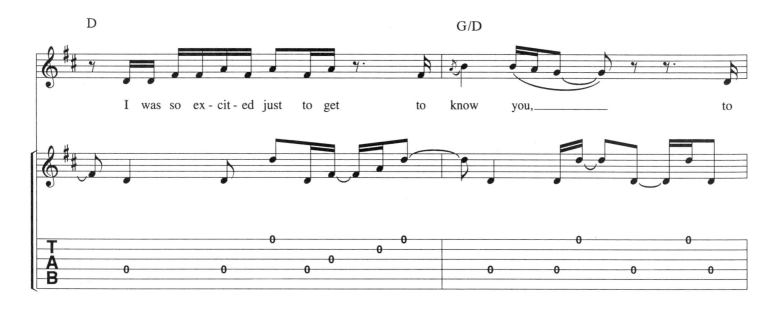

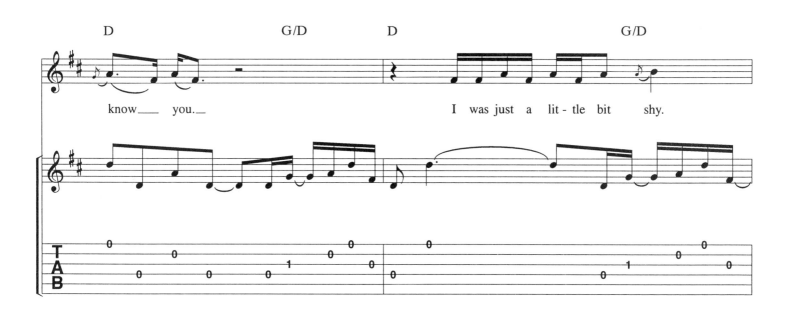

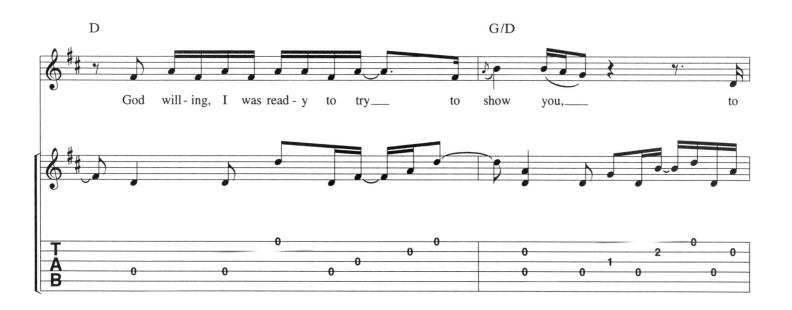

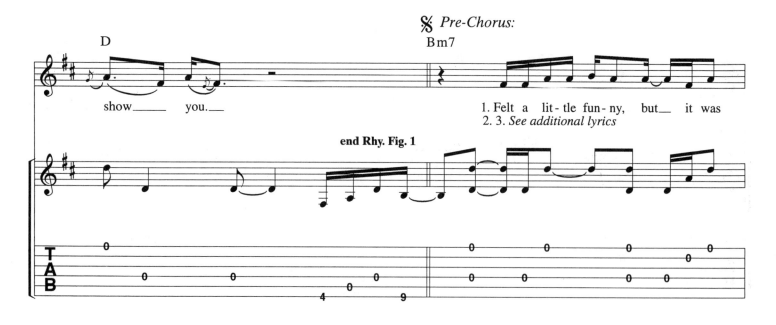

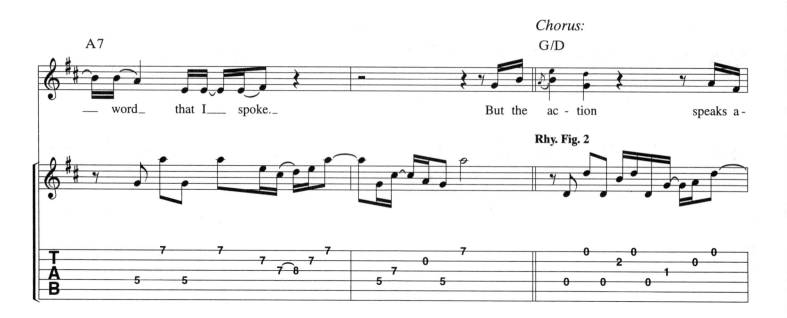

loud - er. The ac - tion___ speaks loud - er___ than the

words. The ac - tion, loud - er than the words.

end Rhy. Fig. 2

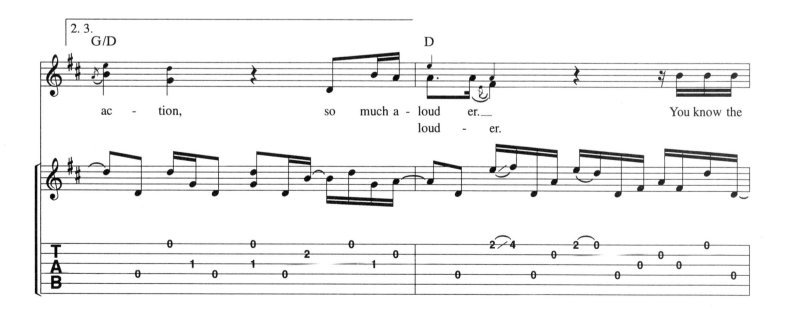

ac - tion, so much a - loud er.___ You know the
loud - er.

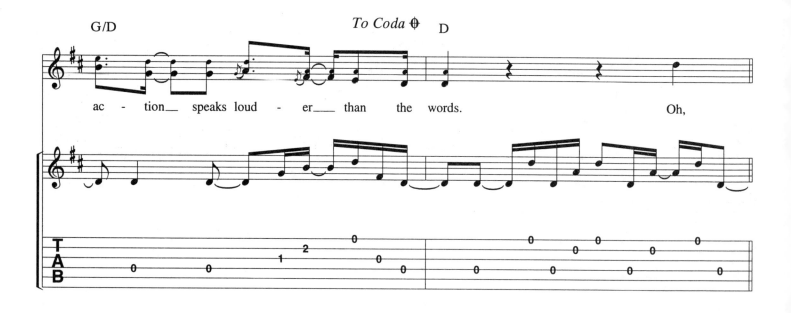

ac - tion__ speaks loud - er__ than the words. Oh,

I can't wait__ un - til__ I'm hold - in' you

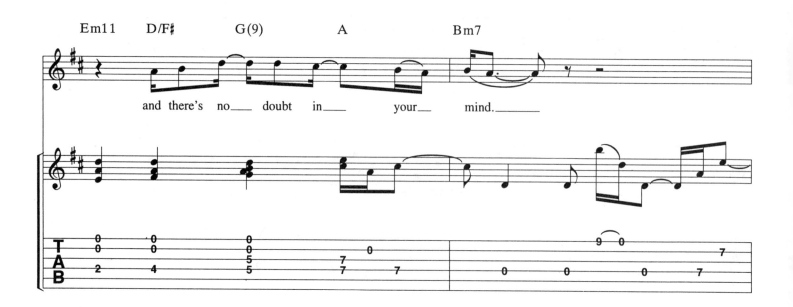

and there's no__ doubt in__ your__ mind.____

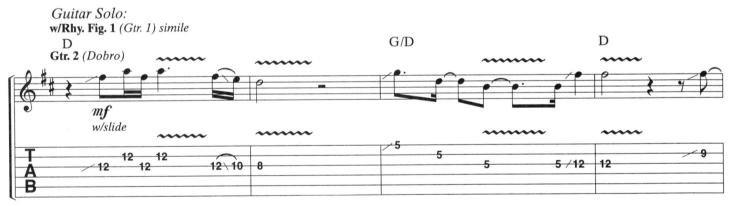

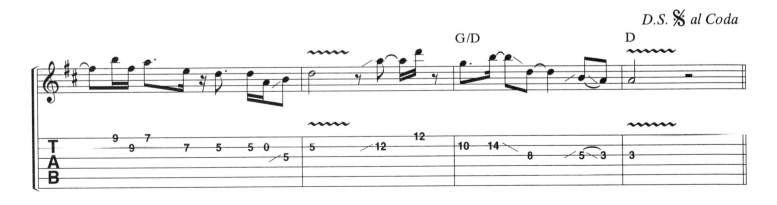

The Action - 8 - 6

Coda

Outro:
w/Rhy. Fig. 2 (Gtr. 1) simile

words.

The ac - tion, loud - er than the

Gtr. 1

Gtr. 2

words.

The ac - tion, loud - er than

w/slide

w/o slide

— the words.

The ac - tion, loud - er than the

w/slide

Verse 2:
I loved you just the way you were.
Somehow, I had to find the nerve
To tell you, oh, baby, just to tell you.
So I did what a man must do,
I walked right over to you,
And I was asking, baby, let's go dancing.

Pre-Chorus 2:
I felt a little guilty,
But I had committed no crime.
I wanted to love you,
Love you and love you for a long, long time.
(To Chorus:)

Pre-Chorus 3:
I'm gonna prove my love
No matter how long that it takes.
'Cause the feelings that I have for you, girl,
Are no mistake.
(To Chorus:)

ALL BY MYSELF

Lyrics by
BILLIE JOE

Music by
BILLIE JOE and GREENDAY

All by Myself - 2 - 1

ALLISON ROAD

By
ROBIN WILSON

Chorus:
Rhythm Figure 2

On

Al - li - son Road. Yeah, I did-n't know I was lost at the time on Al - li - son _ Road. _

Verses 3 & 5:
End Rhythm Figure 2

With Rhythm Figure 2 (Guitar 1)

3. So she fills up her _ sails with my wast - ed breath and each
5. *See additional lyrics*

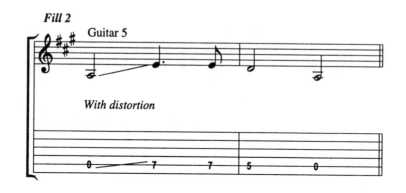

Additional Lyrics

Verse 2: Fools in the rain if the sun gets through,
Fire's in heaven of the eyes I knew on Allison Road.

Verse 5: I lost my mind if the sun gets through,
Fire's in the heaven of the eyes I knew on Allison Road.

CAN'T CRY ANYMORE

Words and Music by
SHERYL CROW and BILL BOTTRELL

Can't Cry Anymore - 4 - 1

Verse 2:
Since I left,
Been feelin' better, cause that's
What you get when you
Stay together too long.
And I can't cry anymore.

Verse 3:
And now I know that,
Money comes in.
But the fact is (there's)
Not enough to pay my taxes.
And I can't cry anymore.

Verse 4:
Well gotta brother.
He's got real problems.
Heroin now,
There's just no stopping him tonight.
And I won't cry anymore.

Verse 5:
Well it could be worse,
I could've missed my calling.
Sometimes it hurts,
But when you read the writing on the wall.
Can't cry anymore.

COME TO MY WINDOW

Lyrics and Music by
MELISSA ETHERIDGE

Come To My Window – 5 – 1

Come To My Window – 5 – 2

Chorus:

Rhy. Fig. 2

Riff A

Come to my win - dow.

(end Rhy. Fig. 2)

Crawl in - side, wait __ by the light __ of the moon.

(end Riff A)

w/Rhy. Fig. 2 _(Gtr. 2)_ **& Riff A** _(Gtr. 1)_

__ Come to my win - dow, I'll __ be home soon. __

1.

Come To My Window – 5 – 3

Come To My Window – 5 – 4

Verse 2:
Keeping my eyes open, I cannot afford to sleep.
Giving away promises I know that I can't keep.
Nothing fills the blackness that has seeped into my chest.
I need you in my blood, I am forsaking all the rest.
Just to reach you,
Just to reach you.
Oh, to reach you.
(To Chorus:)

CREOSOTE

Words and Music by
JAY FARRAR

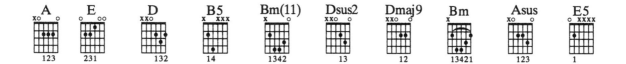

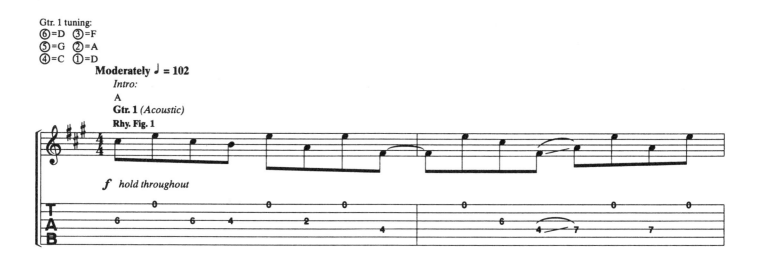

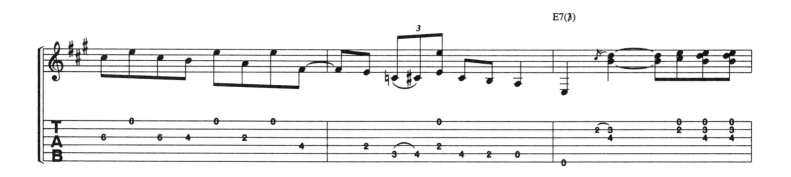

Creosote - 3 - 1

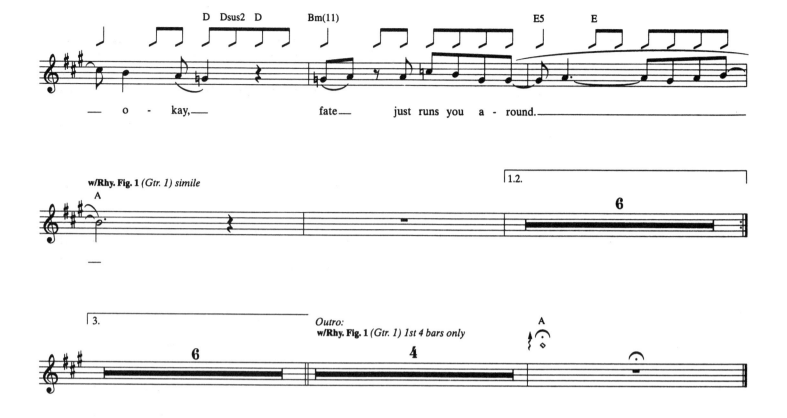

Verse 3:
From Memphis to New Orleans,
In and out of railroad dreams,
You're out there in scenes passing by.
Everyone faces what they deserve,
A carousel to claim or curse,
Sticking around, at least for the ride.
(To Chorus:)

FAR, FAR AWAY

Words and Music by
JEFF TWEEDY

Far, Far Away – 4 – 1

Far, Far Away – 4 – 2

Verse 2:
I long to hold you in my arms and sway,
Kiss and ride on the C.T.A.
I need to see you tonight
In those bright lights.
Well, I know it's right.
(To Chorus:)

Verse 3:
By the bed, by the light that you read by,
By the time I get home to say goodnight.
I need to see you again
On the dark side, my friend,
On the dark side.

FOOLISH GAMES

Words and Music by
JEWEL KILCHER

Outro:
w/Rhy. Fig. 2 *(Gtr. 1)*

You took your coat____ off,

stood in the rain,_____ you're al - ways

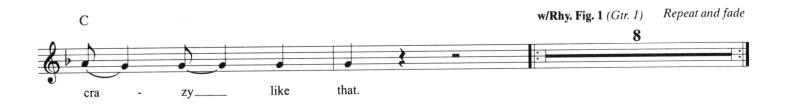

cra - zy____ like that.

w/Rhy. Fig. 1 *(Gtr. 1)*   *Repeat and fade*

Verse 2:
You're always the mysterious one with
Dark eyes and careless hair,
You were fashionably sensitive
But too cool to care.
You stood in my doorway with nothing to say
Besides some comment on the weather.

Verse 3:
You're always brilliant in the morning,
Smoking your cigarettes and talking over coffee.
Your philosophies on art, Baroque moved you.
You loved Mozart and you'd speak of your loved ones
As I clumsily strummed my guitar.

Verse 4:
You'd teach me of honest things,
Things that were daring, things that were clean.
Things that knew what an honest dollar did mean.
I hid my soiled hands behind my back.
Somewhere along the line, I must have gone
Off track with you.

Pre-Chorus 2:
Excuse me, think I've mistaken you for somebody else,
Somebody who gave a damn, somebody more like myself.
(To Chorus:)

FRAGILE

Words and Music by
NANCI GRIFFITH

Fragile - 3 - 1

*Lead vocal tacet 3rd & 4th times.

Verse 2:

I stared up at the faces in the mountain,
Just a year ago.
Laughin' in the spirit of America,
And singin' in the snow.
Now, I wish I felt as strong as that mountain,   (Ah.)
Just carved in stone.
I wish I was the Gulf Stream water,   (Ah.)
I would sail you home.
(To Chorus:)

Verse 3:

I would give you all that's in me,
Though part of me is gone.
If I could have that day upon the mountain,
For the snow and the song.
Here's to love and all that it changes,   (Ah.)
When you're alone out in the storm.
Cuz If I'd had a shield of heather,   (Ah.)
I'd have never loved at all.
(To Chorus:)

GIVING

Words and Music by
ED ROLAND

Giving - 2 - 1

Verse 2:
You're giving me calm to fall into,
Giving me hope to guide me through,
And I want more, I want more.
Giving me light to see through tears,
Giving me strength to crash my fears,
And I want more, I want more.
Still, all I need is love,
So give me more.
(To Chorus:)

Verse 3:
You're giving me choice so I may seek,
Giving me faith so I'll believe,
And I want more, I want more.
Giving me breath of your mercy,
Giving yourself to comfort me,
And I want more, I want more.
Still, all I need is love,
So give me more.
(To Outro:)

THE GOLDEN AGE

Words and Music by
DAVID LOWERY and JOHN HICKMAN

*Pedal steel gtr. arr. for gtr. (Gtr. 1 simile 2nd time.)

**Baritone gtr. arr. for gtr. (Sounds one octave lower than written.)

This is ___ the gold-en age, it's hard to i-mag-ine with the way ___ I feel ___ to-day. ___ But this ___ is the gold-en age, ___ the gold-en age.

The Golden Age - 2 - 1

GONE CRAZY

Words and Music by
JOHN WOZNIAK

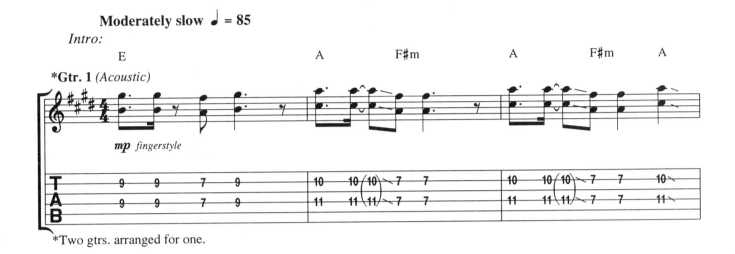

*Two gtrs. arranged for one.

Come back _ and be,   come back _ for free,

come back _ and stay; child, have   you _ gone _ cra - zy?

Gone Crazy – 4 – 1

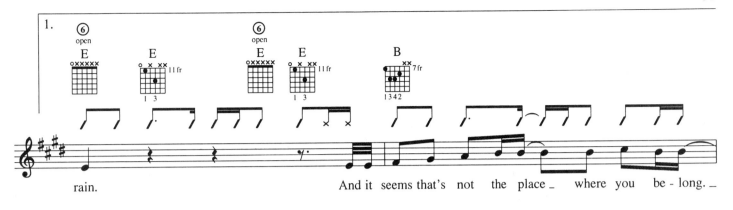

rain.   And it seems that's not the place _ where you be - long. _

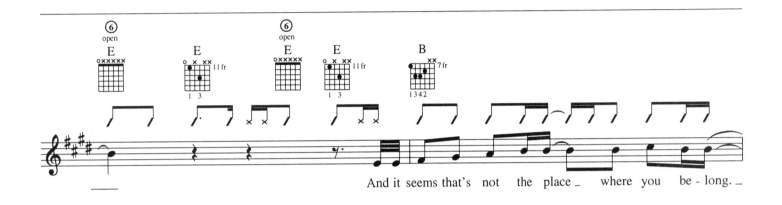

And it seems that's not the place _ where you be - long. _

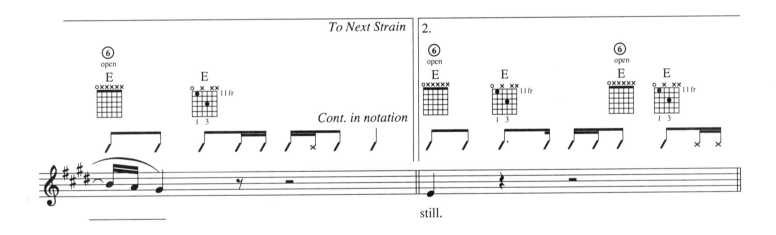

To Next Strain   2.

Cont. in notation

still.

Chorus:

When there's _ no sun,   and there's _ no moon,

Gtr. 1

Gone Crazy – 4 – 3

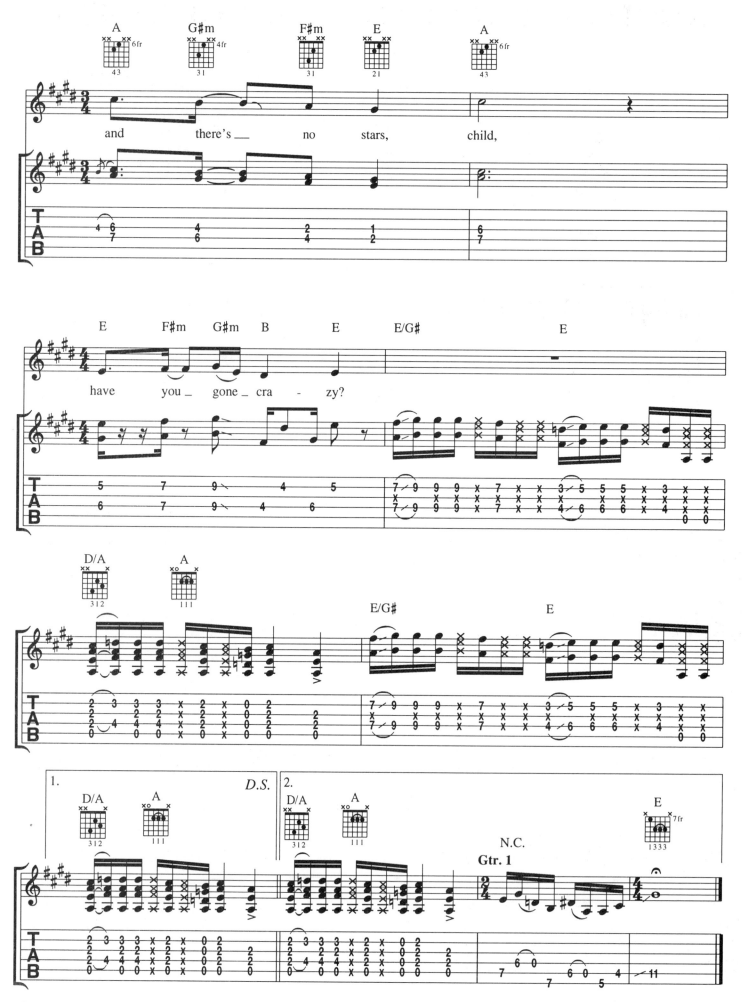

Gone Crazy – 4 – 4

GOOD RIDDANCE (TIME OF YOUR LIFE)

Lyrics by
BILLIE JOE

Music by
BILLIE JOE and GREENDAY

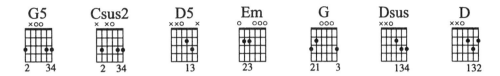

Fast ♩ = 172

Intro:
G5

Gtr. 1 *(Acoustic)*

mf *hold throughout*

Verse:
G5

Gtr. 1 cont. rhy. simile

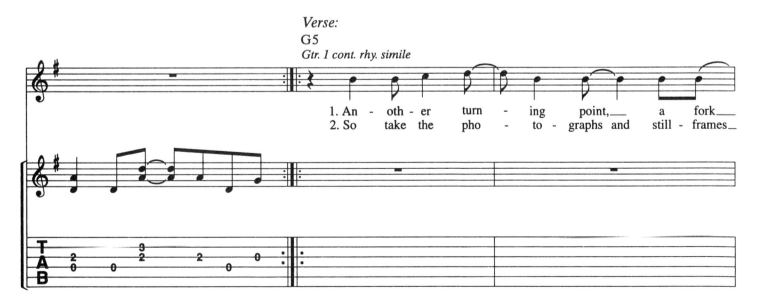

1. An - oth - er turn - ing point,___ a fork___
2. So take the pho - to - graphs and still - frames___

Good Riddance (Time of Your Life) - 3 - 1

Good Riddance (Time of Your Life) - 3 - 3

I'M THE ONLY ONE

Lyrics & Music by
MELISSA ETHERIDGE

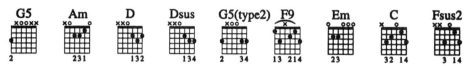

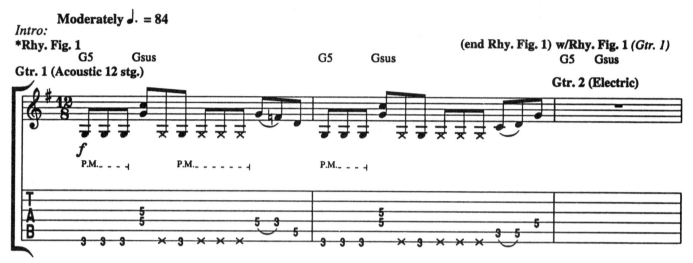

*When played on 12 string guitar some notes will sound one octave higher than written.

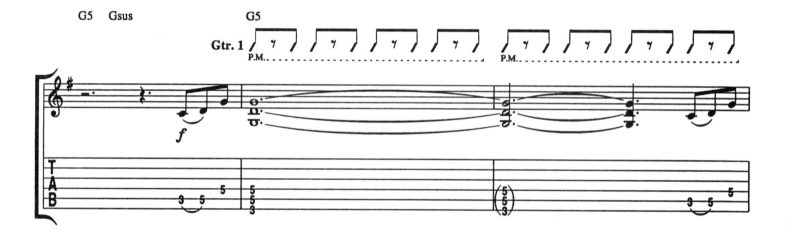

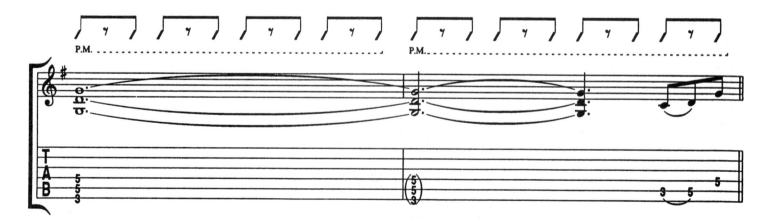

Verse:

Gtr. 1 G5

1. Please ba-by, can't you see my mind's a burn-ing hell? I got
2. *See additional lyrics.*

Rhy. Fig. 2a

ra-zor's a-rip-pin' and tear-in' and strip-pin' my heart a-part as well.

Rhy. Fig. 2

w/ Rhy. Figs. 2 (Gtr. 2) & 2a (gtr. 1) both 2 times

To-night you told me that you ache for some-thing new. And some oth-er wom-an is look-in' like some-thing that might be good for you.

Pre-Chorus:

Gtr. 1 Am   D   Dsus

(Cont. rhy. simile)

Go on and hold her 'til the scream-ing is gone.

Gtr. 2

hold

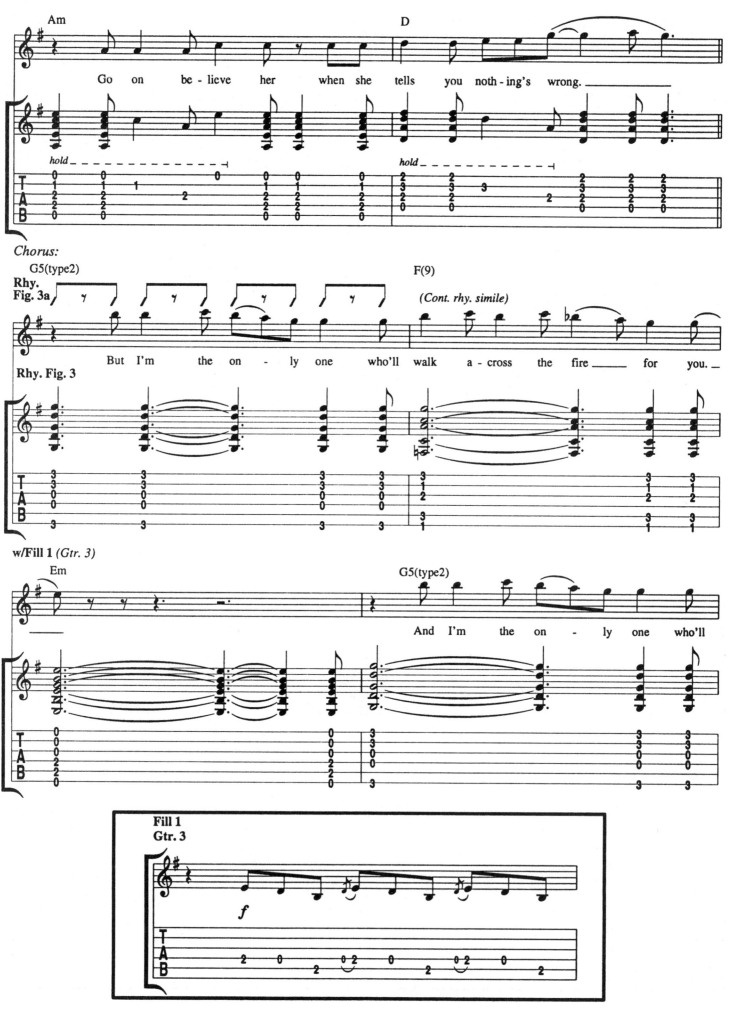

Chorus:

Go on be-lieve her when she tells you noth-ing's wrong.

But I'm the on-ly one who'll walk a-cross the fire for you.

And I'm the on-ly one who'll

I'm The Only One - 6 - 4

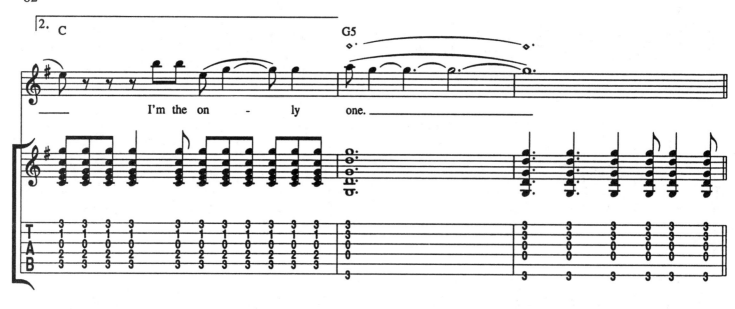

I'm the on - ly one. ___

Guitar Solo:

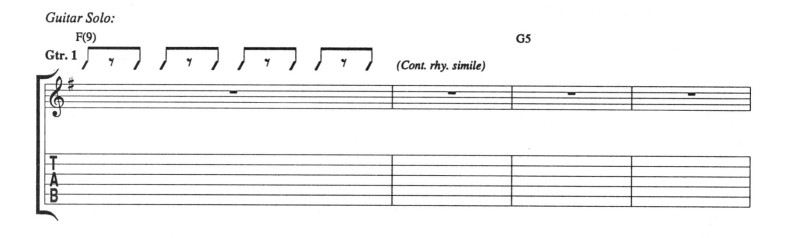

(Cont. rhy. simile)

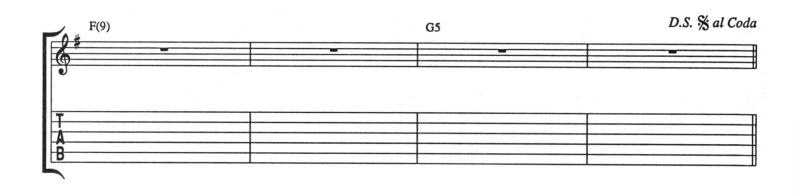

D.S. 𝄋 al Coda

Coda

w/Rhy. Figs. 3 (Gtr. 2) & 3a (Gtr. 1)

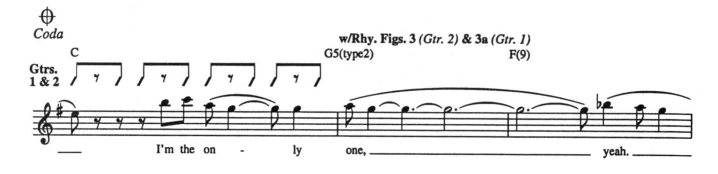

___ I'm the on - ly one, ___ yeah. ___

w/Fill 1 *(Gtr. 3)*

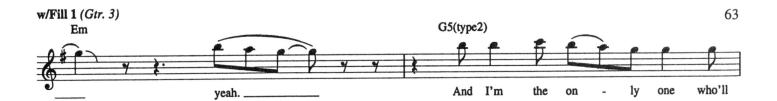

yeah. _____ And I'm the on - ly one who'll

w/Fill 1 *(Gtr. 3)*

drown _ in my de-sire for you. ___ It's on - ly fear that makes_ you run the

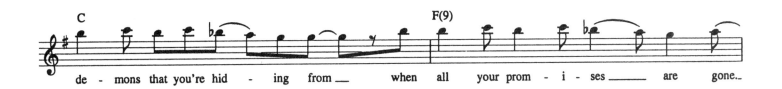

de - mons that you're hid - ing from ___ when all your prom - i - ses _____ are gone._

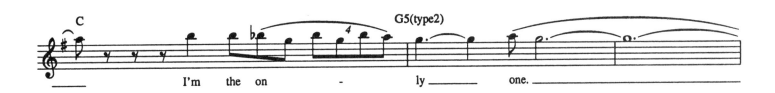

___ I'm the on - ly _____ one. _____

Outro:

ad lib. vocal until fade

Repeat & Fade

I'm the on-ly one,_babe.

Gtr. 2

P.M. - - - -

Verse 2:

Please baby, can't you see I'm trying to explain.
I've been here before and I'm locking the door and
I'm not going back again.
Her eyes and arms and skin won't make it go away.
You'll wake up tomorrow and wrestle the sorrow
that holds you down today.

(To Pre-Chorus:)

I WANT TO COME OVER

Words and Music by
MELISSA ETHERIDGE

* Chords implied by bass/keybd.
** On 2nd verse.

A   Asus2

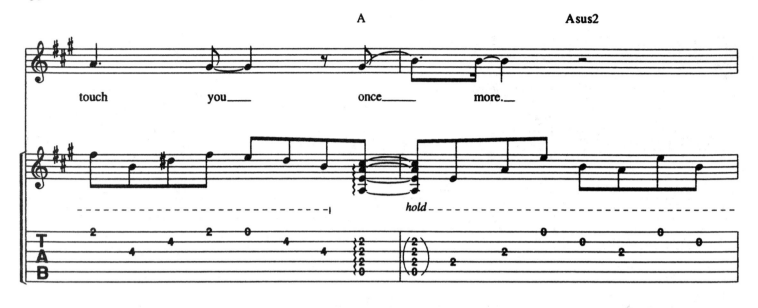

touch   you___   once___   more.___

Gtr. 2 (w/dist.)

A5

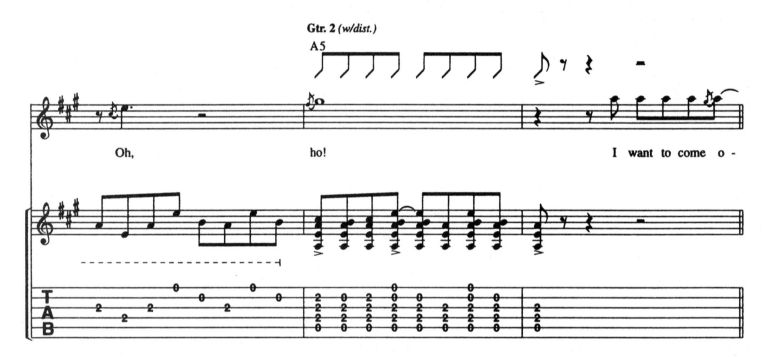

Oh,   ho!   I want to come o-

Chorus:

Gtr. 4
(Acoustic)

E   C#m

Cont. rhy. simile

-ver,   to hell with the con - se - quence.

Rhy. Fig. 3
* Gtrs. 1, 2 and 3

mf
hold

*Two gtrs. arranged for one.

I Want to Come Over - 8 - 3

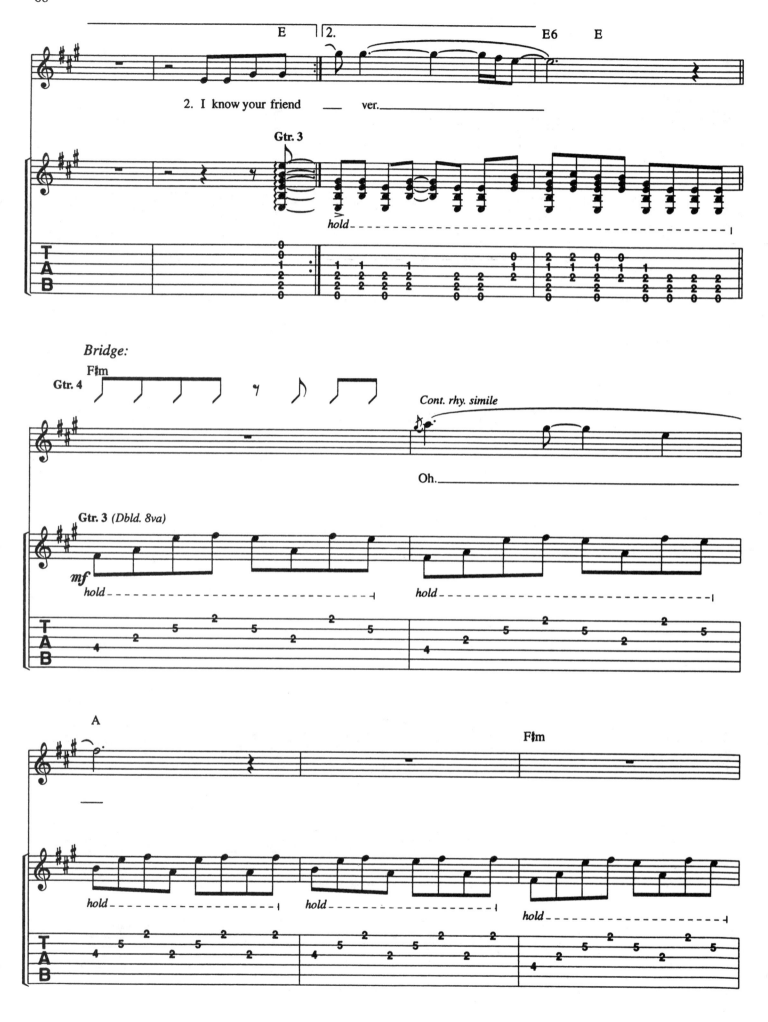

2. I know your friend ___ ver._____

Bridge:

Oh._____

Verse 2:
I know your friend.
You told her about me.
She filled you with fear,
Some kind of sin.
How can you turn,
Denying the fire?
Lover I burn,
Let me in.
(To Chorus:)

Verse 3:
I know you're confused,
I know that you're shaken,
You think we'll be lost
Once we begin.
I know you're weak.
I know that you want me.
Lover don't speak,
Let me in.
(To Chorus:)

JUST LIKE YOU

Words and Music by
KEVIN MOORE and JOHN LEWIS PARKER

All gtrs. capo V

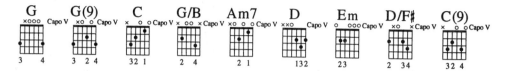

Moderately ♩ = 116

Intro:

*Gtr. 1 (Acoustic)

*Fingerstyle throughout.

Verse 1:

Hel - lo, my friend,___ it's___ been___ a while.___

Just Like You - 10 - 1

Verses 2 & 3:

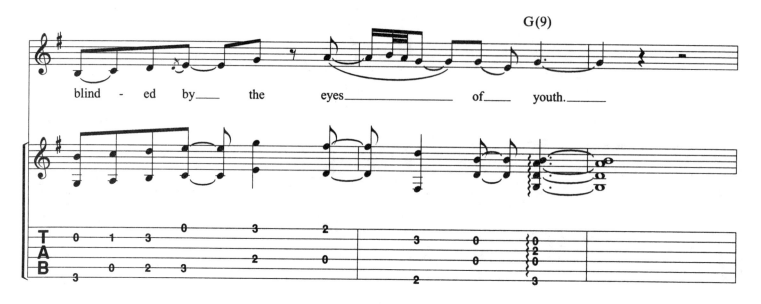

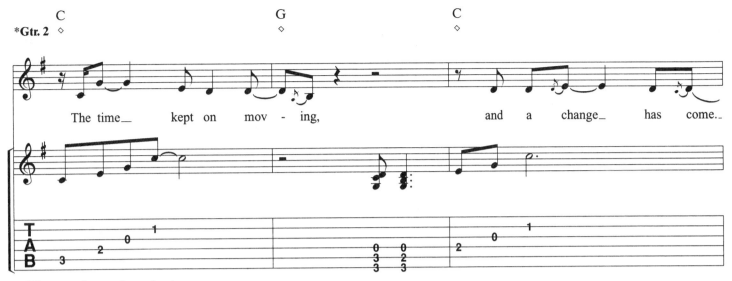

*Piano arr. for gtr. throughout.

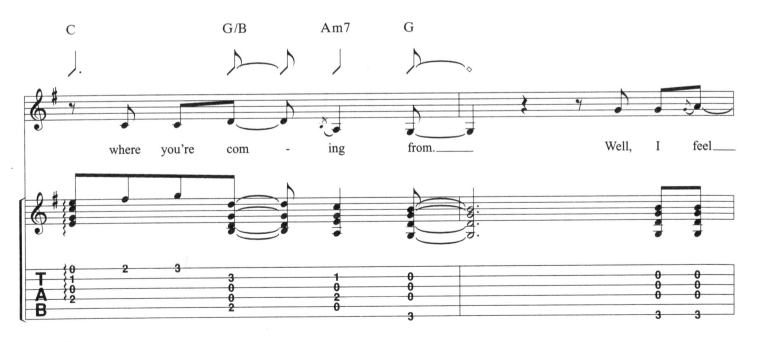

Chorus:

Am7

And un-der my_____ skin.

1. D/F# Csus2

I'm just like a-you._____

trem. bar

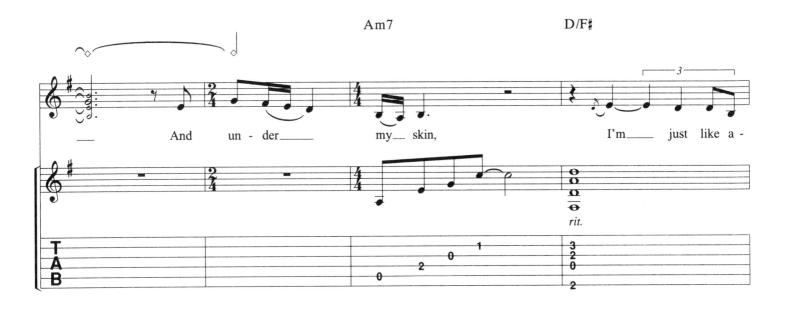

And un-der_____ my_ skin, I'm_____ just like a-

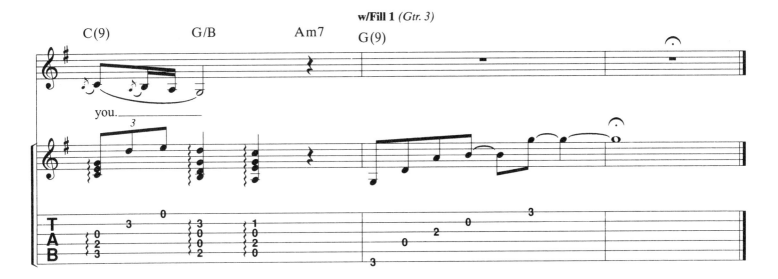

you.____

w/Fill 1 (Gtr. 3)

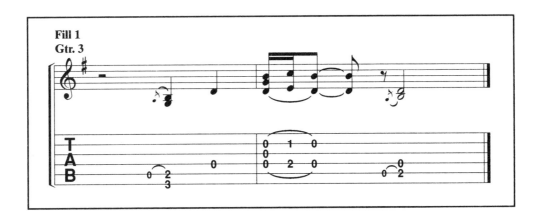

Fill 1
Gtr. 3

Verse 3:
You gave your love and your innocence,
And they took away your confidence.
I'm not those women,
And I'm not those men.
Put your arms around me.
I am your friend.
(To Chorus:)

LEAVING LAS VEGAS

Words and Music by
**SHERYL CROW, KEVIN GILBERT,
BILL BOTTRELL, DAVID BAERWALD** and **DAVID RICKETTS**

Leaving Las Vegas - 7 - 1

Leav-ing Las Veg - as.

Leav-ing for good... for good. I'm leav-ing for

Gtr. 1 doubles Gtr. 2 for next 4 measures

good. I'm leav-ing for

Gtrs. 1 & 2*

P.M. P.M. P.M.

good.

P.M. P.M.

Leaving Las Vegas - 7 - 4

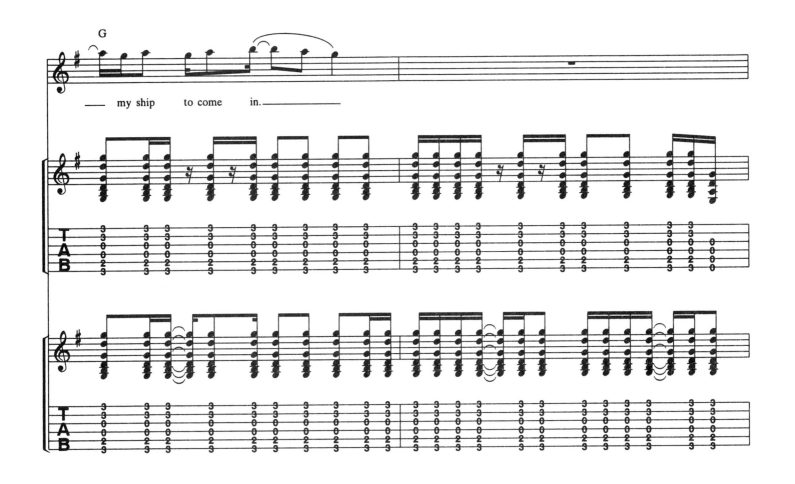

my ship to come in.

But now no jok - er, no jack, no— king,

Leaving Las Vegas - 7 - 6

Verse 3:
Quit my job as a dancer,
At the Lido des Girls,
Dealing blackjack until one or two.
Such a muddy line between,
The things you want,
And the things you have to do.
(To Chorus 4:)

Leaving Las Vegas - 7 - 7

LEFT A SLIDE

Words and Music by
JAY FARRAR

Gtr. 1 tuned down 1/2 step:
⑥=E♭ ③=G♭
⑤=A♭ ②=B♭
④=D♭ ①=E♭

Slow ♩ = 62

Left a Slide - 3 - 1

Weight-ed down,_____ the nail__ be-low__ the head._____

Pedal-Steel Solo:

E-nough con-cern_____ to ride_____ it

out, it's no sur-prise_____ that it's a long,_____

slow fade._____

Verse 2:
It gets so diffused, you want to kiss the ground
And leave no sound, make it up the next year.
Chalk it up to remember, the wasted lonely fever.
The way we've tried, left a slide into harm's way.

Verse 3:
Minefield is the word from the start,
Watching out for the worst.
Never clear till it hurts.
Call it off to make amends,
This life burns down from both ends.
The way we've tried,
Left a slide into harm's way.
(To Chorus:)

MISERY

Words and Music by
DAVID PIRNER

Moderately ♩ = 108

Intro:

*Bass plays D, E.

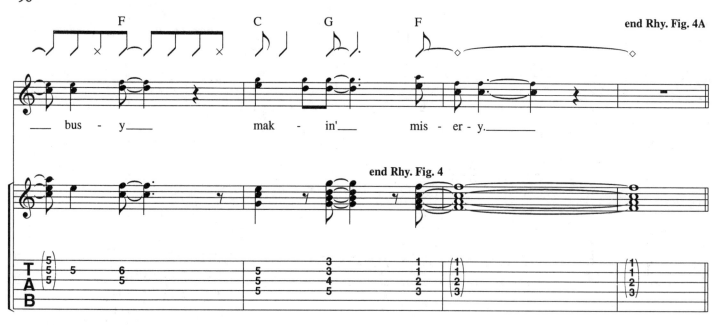

bus - y___ mak - in'___ mis - er - y.___

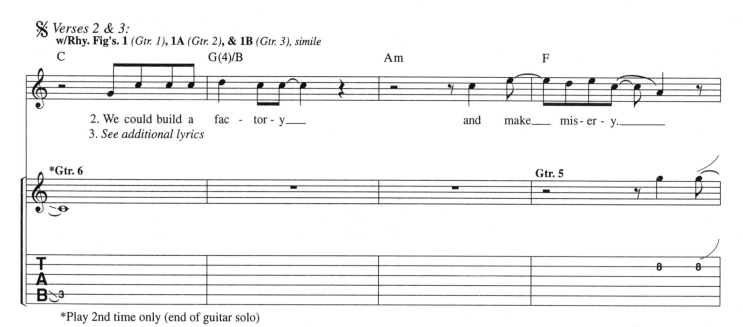

Verses 2 & 3:
w/Rhy. Fig's. 1 (Gtr. 1), 1A (Gtr. 2), & 1B (Gtr. 3), simile

2. We could build a fac - tor - y___ and make___ mis - er - y.___
3. See additional lyrics

*Play 2nd time only (end of guitar solo)

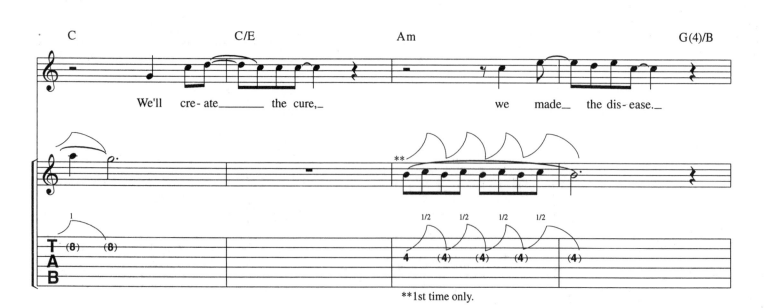

We'll cre - ate_____ the cure,_ we made_ the dis - ease._

**1st time only.

need.

Yeah, yeah,___ mis -

\- er - y.

I'm not used___ to my friends.

*Bass plays D.

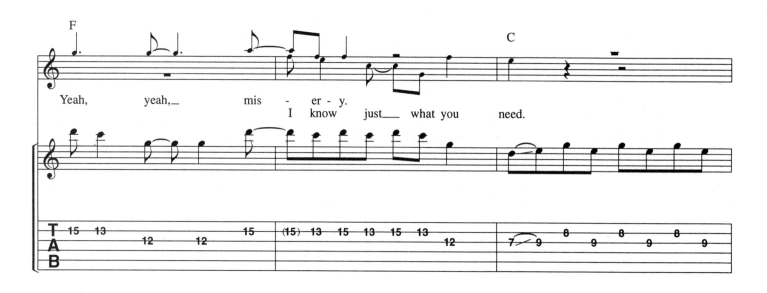

Yeah, yeah,___ mis - er - y.

I know just___ what you need.

Verse 3:
Yet you satisfy your greed
Get what you need.
There's lonely envy,
So empty.

NEW THING NOW

Words and Music by
SHAWN COLVIN

New Thing Now - 7 - 1

New Thing Now - 7 - 6

not quite.

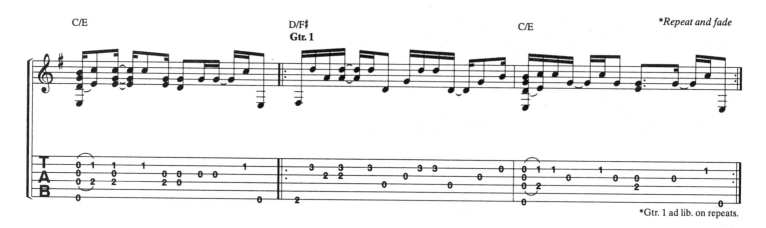

Repeat and fade

Gtr. 1

*Gtr. 1 ad lib. on repeats.

Verse 2:
Gee, it's good to see a dream come true,
People smile and bless all over you.
Mixing up those latest junkie-isms,
All the pretty terms of religion.
And don't you love the leader of the band,
Equal parts Butthead and Peter Pan?
All the other kids are sad again,
And a legend's not a legend till it ends.

Chorus 3:
This is your new thing now,
And it makes the whole world spin.
It's at least as old as sin, but not quite.
This is your new thing now.
And now you're turning, grinning,
But maybe no one's listening,
And you might lose it all, my darling, yes, you might.
(To Chorus 4:)

NO MORE PARADES

Words and Music by
JAY FARRAR

*Gtr. 1 tuned:
⑥=D ③=G
⑤=A ②=B
④=D ①=D
*Capo at 2nd fret to
match recording.

Moderately fast ♩ = 176

Intro:

Gtr. 1 (Acoustic)

Verse:

w/Rhy. Fig. 1 (Gtr. 1) 4 times, simile

1. Don't know if you're car - ing. _____ The
2.3. See additional lyrics

truth is we're tear - ing, and we're _____ miles _____ a - part. _____

Front door _____ leav - ing _____ is the

way _____ I've been feel - ing, _____ twen - ty days _____

No More Parades - 3 - 1

Verse 2:
Got to know a friend
With a think-tank and a farm,
And you couldn't ask for better.
Works on dreams, insider schemes,
Lives like the words in a song.
(To Chorus:)

Verse 3:
A pesticide moon hangs,
Cold coffee and tears flow in and out of the brain.
Should've caught the bus, should've pulled the line,
Should've made up for the downtime.
(To Chorus:)

NOBODY'S ANGEL

Words and Music by
NANCI GRIFFITH

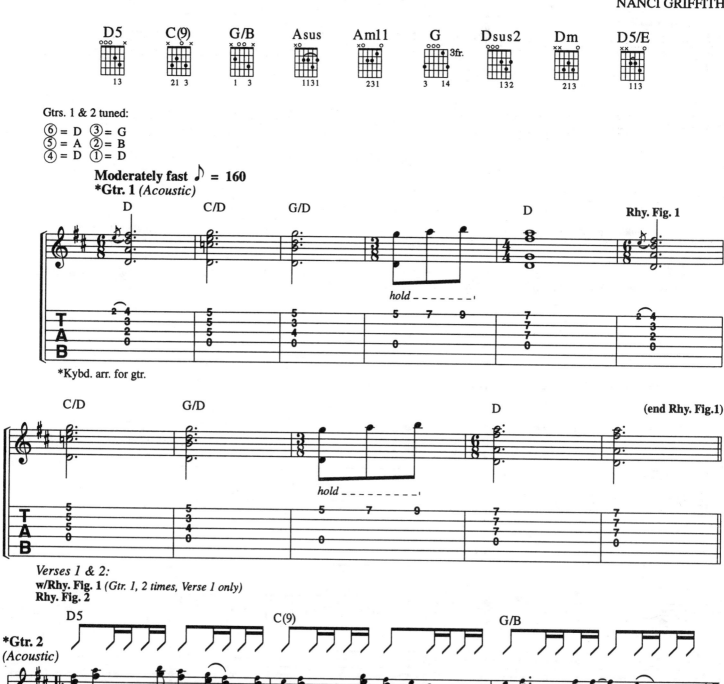

*Rhy. Fig. 2 & Riff A on Verse 2 only.

Nobody's Angel - 6 - 1

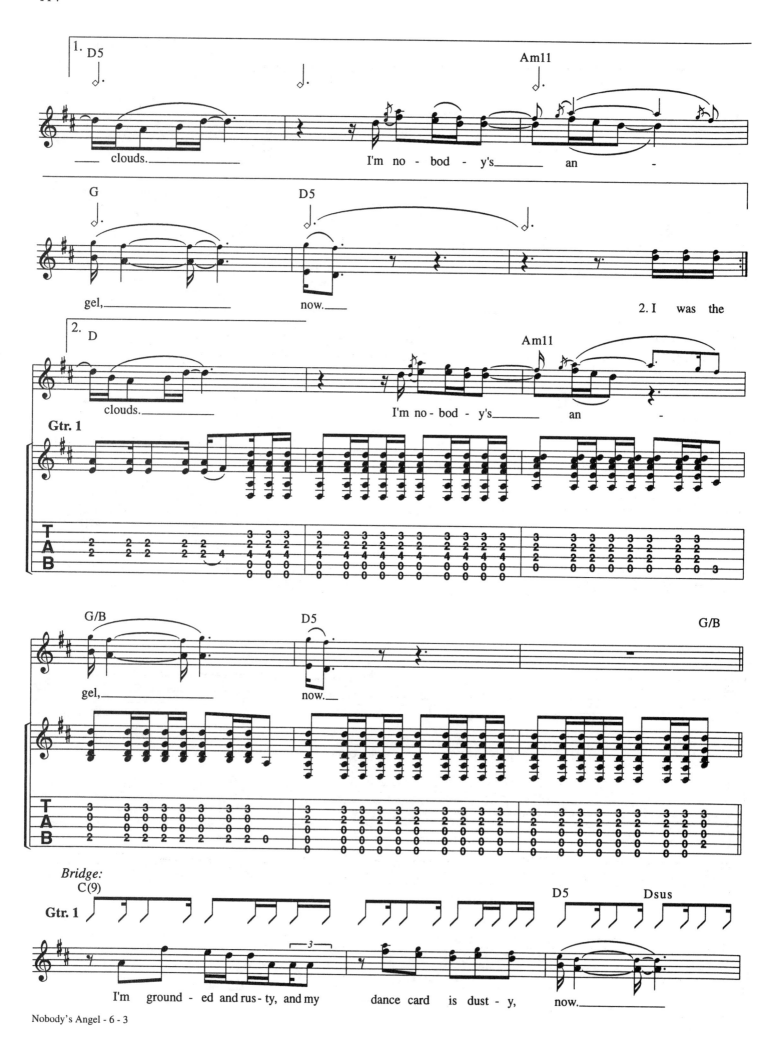

out of the coun - try now.____ I'm

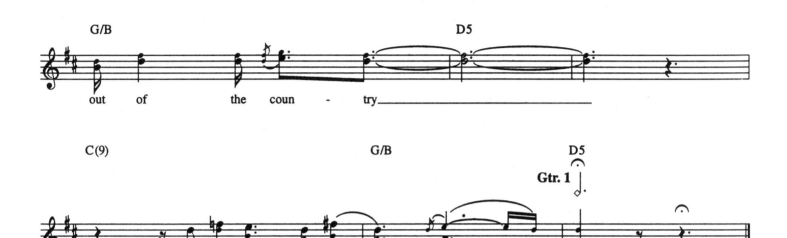

out of the coun - try____

I'm no - bod - y's an - gel,_____ now.

Verse 2:

I was the forest for love songs.
The one who can't love wrong.
The one who won't fall,
But will still write it down.
I'm the one who would understand
Who listens with the pen in hand.
Everyone's shoulder,
Till it's me who falls down.

(To Chorus:)

ONE HEADLIGHT

Words and Music by
JAKOB DYLAN

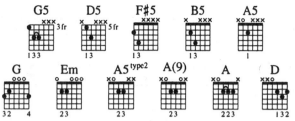

Gtr. 1 tuned:

⑥ – D ③ – G
⑤ – A ② – B
④ – D ① – E

Gtr. 3 (Dobro) tuned:

⑥ – D ③ – G
⑤ – G ② – B
④ – D ① – D

Moderately ♩ = 106

Intro:

1. So long a-go, I don't re-mem-ber when, ___ that's
2. *See additional lyrics*

when they say I lost ___ my on-ly friend. ___ Well, they said she died eas-y of a

One Headlight – 7 – 1

bro - ken - heart dis - ease, as I lis - tened through the cem - e - ter - y trees.

2. I ___ seen the

2. Hey, ___

Chorus:

___ come on, try a lit - tle, noth - in' is for - ev - er. There's got to be ___ some - thin'

*2 gtrs. arr. for 1.

One Headlight – 7 – 2

Outro:

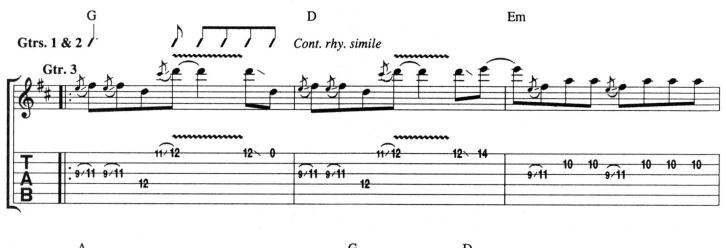

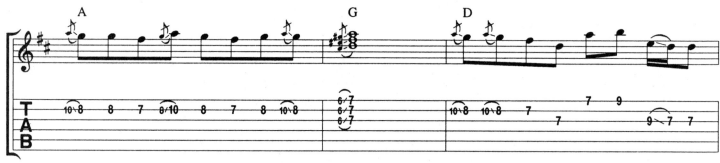

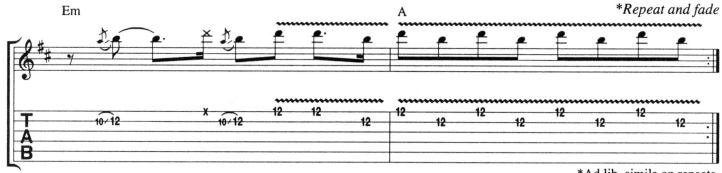

*Ad lib. simile on repeats.

Verse 2:
I seen the sun comin' up at the funeral at dawn,
Of the long broken arm of human law.
Now, it always seemed such a waste,
She always had a pretty face;
I wondered why she hung around this place.
(To Chorus:)

Verse 5:
This place is old, and it feels just like a beat-up truck.
I turn the engine, but the engine doesn't turn.
It smells of cheap wine and cigarettes,
This place is always such a mess;
Sometimes I think I'd like to watch it burn.

Verse 6:
Now I sit alone, and I feel just like somebody else.
Man, I ain't changed, but I know I ain't the same.
But somewhere here, in between these city walls of dying dreams,
I think her death, it must be killing me.
(To Chorus:)

ONE MORE SUICIDE

Words and Music by
JOHN WOZNIAK

One More Suicide – 4 – 1

clutch-ing his Bi - ble and a let - ter ___ from _ her,
clutch-ing her Bi - ble and a let - ter ___ from _ him,

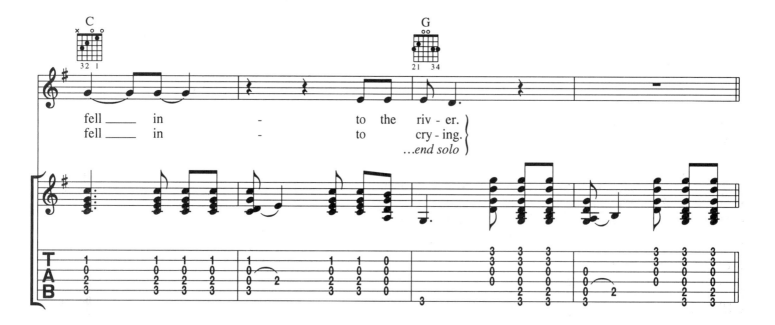

fell ___ in - to the riv - er.
fell ___ in - to cry - ing.
...end solo

Pre-Chorus:

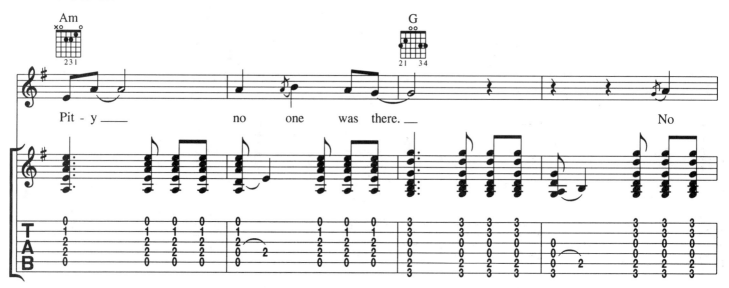

Pit - y ___ no one was there. ___ No

One More Suicide – 4 – 3

One more su - i - cide, _

yeah. _____

One more su - i - cide, _ yeah. _

One More Suicide – 4 – 4

ONE OF US

Words and Music by
ERIC BAZILIAN

All gtrs. Capo II

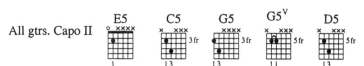

Moderately slow ♩ = 88

A cappella singing (excerpt
from "The Airplane Ride "
by Nell Hampton).

Intro:

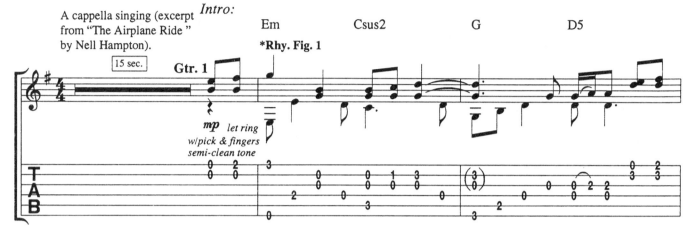

*All repeats and recalled guitar figures ad lib. simile (throughout).

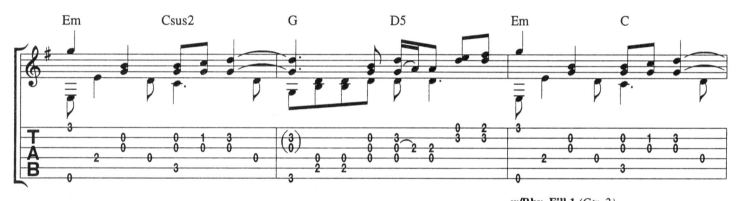

w/Rhy. Fill 1 *(Gtr. 2)*

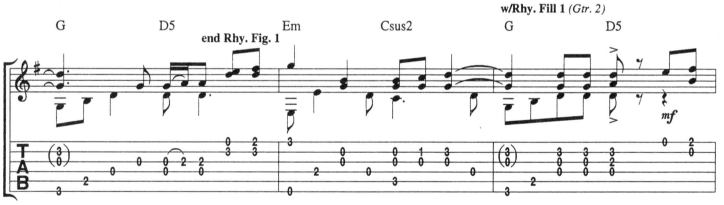

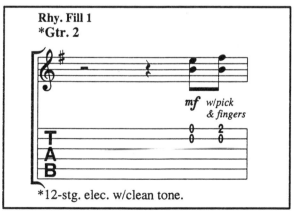

*12-stg. elec. w/clean tone.

One of Us – 7 – 1

130

One of Us – 7 – 5

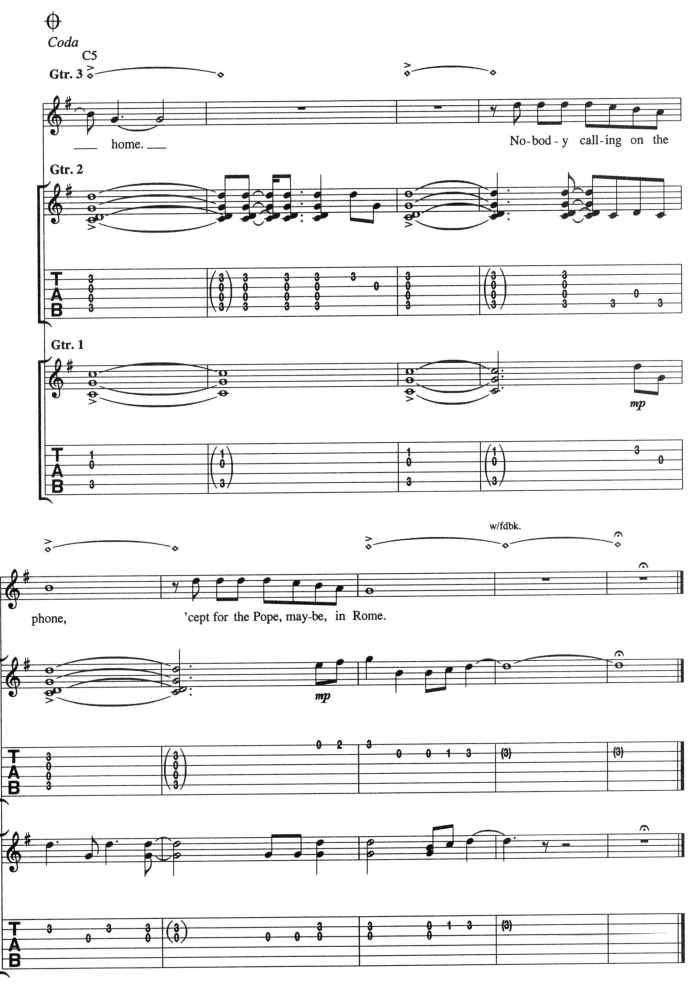

ONLY HAPPY WHEN IT RAINS

Words and Music by
DOUG ERICKSON, SHIRLEY MANSON,
STEVE MARKER and BUTCH VIG

*Doubled simile by fuzz bass (throughout).

Only Happy When It Rains - 10 - 1

Chorus 1:

Verse 2:

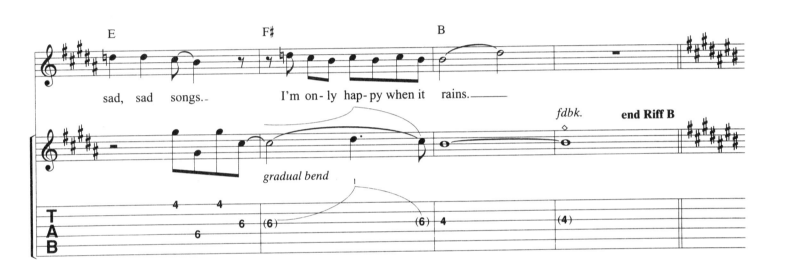

Guitar Solo:

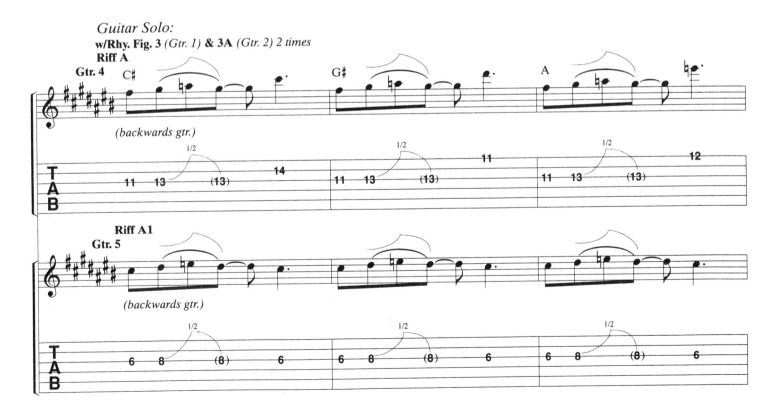

140

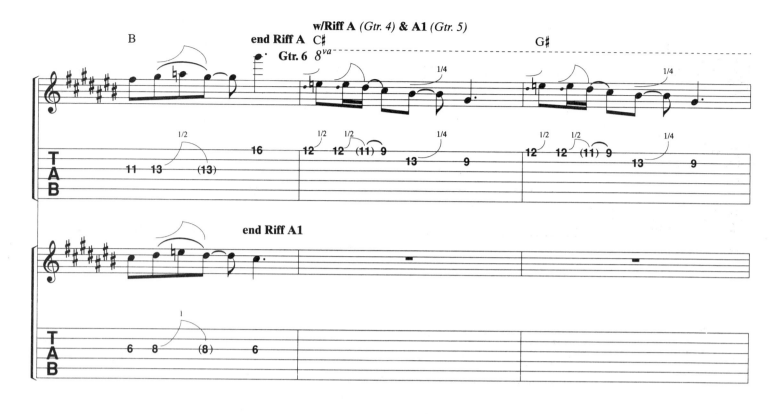

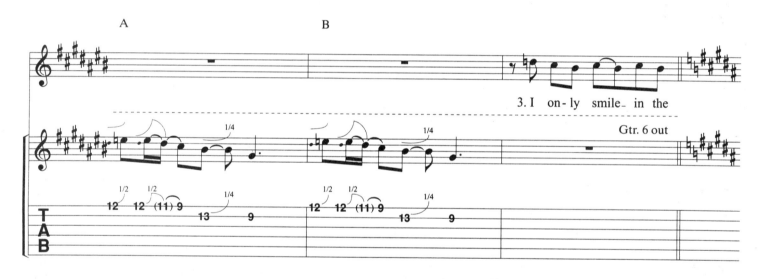

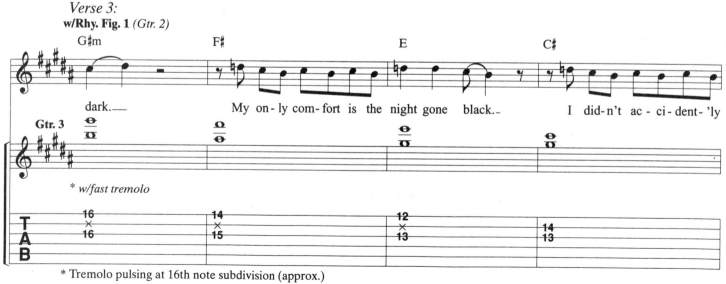

Only Happy When It Rains - 10 - 5

w/**Riff B** (*Gtr. 4*)

E
tell you that.—

F#
I'm on-ly hap-py when it rains.—

G#m

F#
You'll get the mes-sage by the time I'm through.—

E

C#m
When I com-plain a-bout

E
me and you.—

F#
I'm on-ly hap-py when it rains.—

B

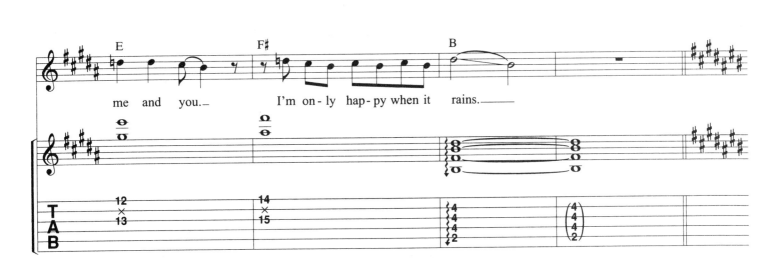

Chorus 2:

*w/**Rhy. Figs 3** (*Gtr.1*) & **3a** & **4** (*Gtr. 2*) *3 times*
w/**Rhy Fig 4** (*Gtr. 3*) *3 times*

C#
Pour your mis-er-y down.—
(Pour— your mis-er-y down.—

G#

A
Pour your mis-er-y down— on
Pour— your

B

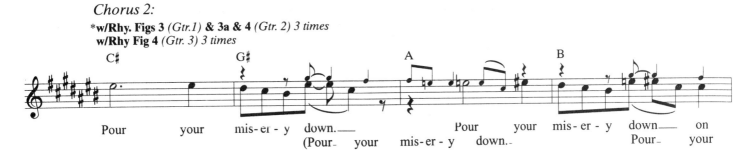

*Gtr. 3 discontinue tremolo effect.

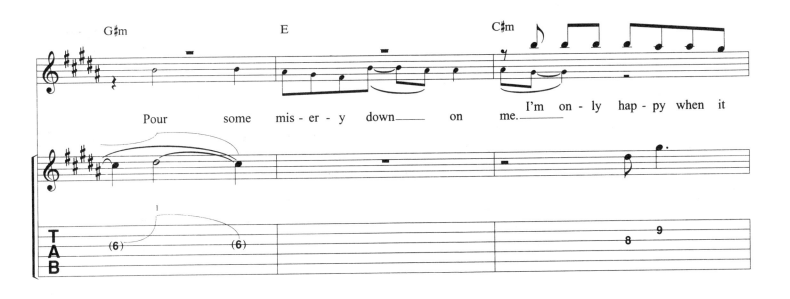

w/Rhy. Figs. 5 *(Gtr. 1)* **&5A** *(Gtr. 2)*
w/Riff C *(Gtr. 4)*

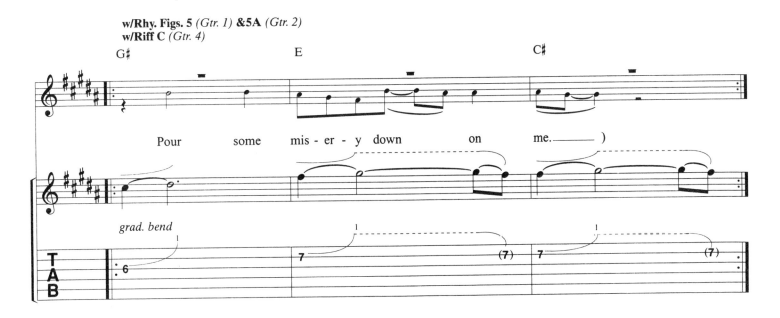

OUTTA MIND (OUTTA SIGHT)

Words and Music by
JEFF TWEEDY

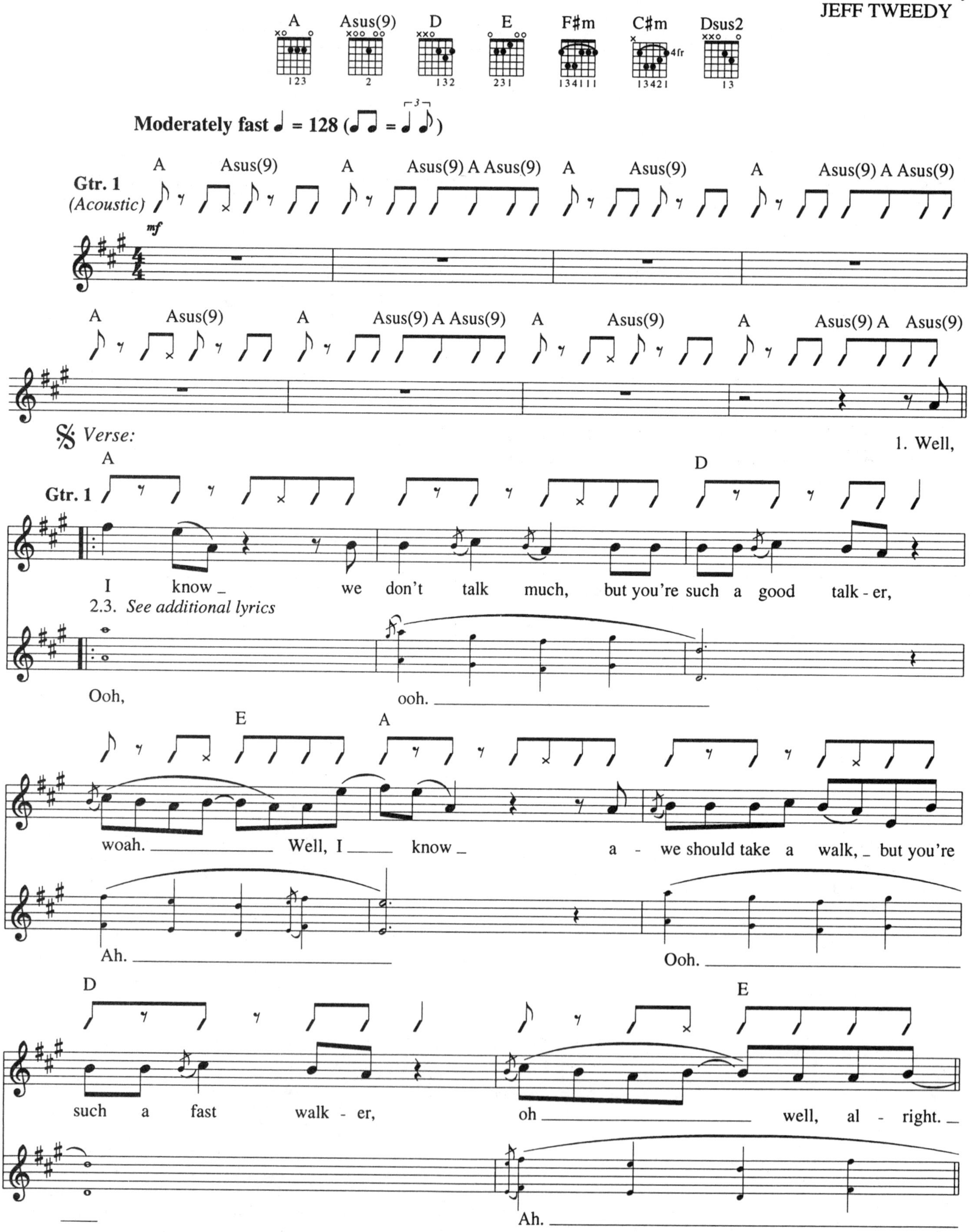

Moderately fast ♩ = 128

Verse:

1. Well, I know _ we don't talk much, but you're such a good talk-er,

2.3. *See additional lyrics*

Ooh, ooh. _

woah. _ Well, I _ know _ a - we should take a walk, _ but you're

Ah. _ Ooh.

such a fast walk-er, oh _ well, al - right. _

Ah. _

Outta Mind (Outta Sight) - 4 - 1

Outta Mind (Outta Sight) – 4 – 2

148

Outta Mind (Outta Sight) – 4 – 3

Coda

Out-ta mind, out-ta sight, _ out-ta mind, out-ta sight. ___

Out-ta mind, out-ta sight. _

Ah. ___

Outro:

*right. _

Well, al-right. _

That's quite al-

**Repeat and fade

*Tacet 1st time.

**Lead vocal ad lib. simile.

Verse 2:
Well, okay, I know you don't love me,
But you still been thinkin' of me. Oh, oh. (Ah.)
Well, alright, I know you probably hate me.
Well, that's okay with me. (Ah.)
(To Chorus:)

Verse 3:
Well, lookout, well, here I come again,
And I'm bringin' my friends. (Ah.)
I said lookout. Well, here I come again,
And I'm bringin' my friends. (Ah.)
Okay, alright, okay, alright.
(To Chorus:)

RUN - AROUND

By JOHN POPPER

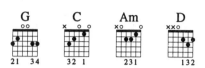

Moderately fast ♩ = 150

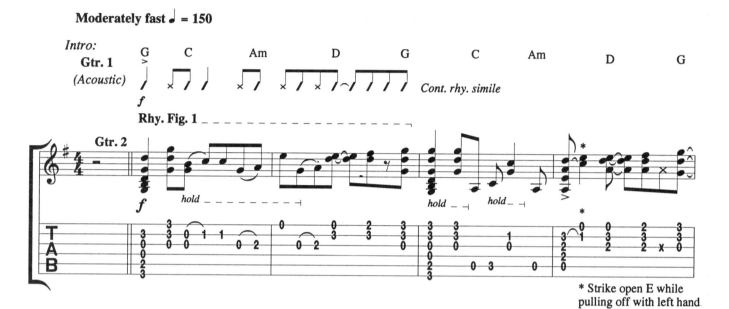

* Strike open E while
pulling off with left hand.

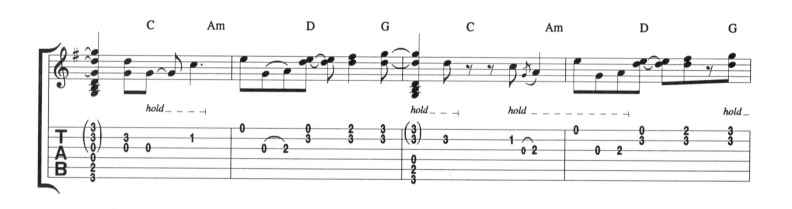

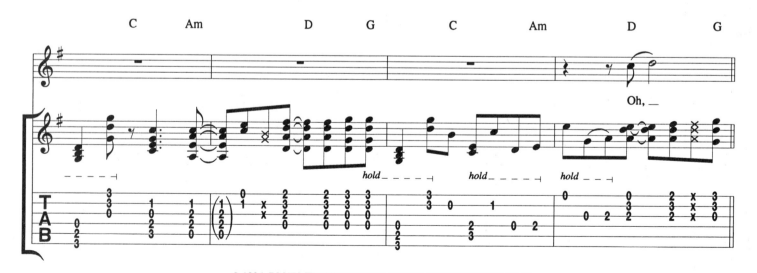

Oh, —

Pre-Chorus:

Chorus:

give me a run - a - round? ___ Is ___ it a sure - fire way to speed _ things up, ___ when

all it does is ___ slow _____ me ___ down?

Harmonica Solo:

Run - Around – 6 – 4

Verse 2:
And shake me and my confidence
About a great many things.
But I've been there, I can see it cower
Like a nervous magician waiting in the wings.
Of a bad play where the heroes are right,
And nobody thinks or expects too much,
And Hollywood's calling for the movie rights,
Singing, "Hey babe, let's keep in touch,
Hey baby, let's keep in touch."

Pre - Chorus:
But I want more than a touch,
I want you to reach me,
And show me all the things no one else can see.
So what you feel becomes mine as well,
And soon if we're lucky we'd be unable to tell
What's yours and mine, the fishing's fine,
And it doesn't have to rhyme, so don't you
Feed me a line.

(To Chorus:)

SEX AND CANDY

Words and Music by
JOHN WOZNIAK

Moderately slow ♩ = 80

Verse :

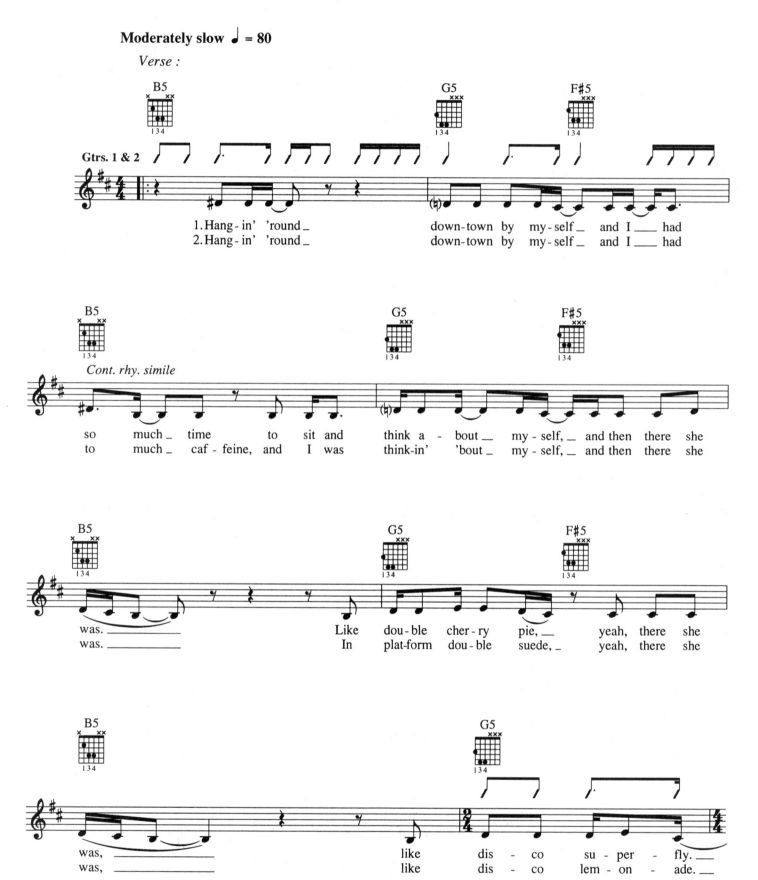

SHE TALKS TO ANGELS

Words and Music by
CHRIS ROBINSON and
RICH ROBINSON

She Talks to Angels - 4 - 1

Oh oh, she talks to an - gels.

They call her out, yeah yeah, call her out. Don't you know that they call her out by her name.

Additional Lyrics

3. She keeps a lock of hair in her pocket.
   She wears a cross around her neck.
   The hair is from a little boy,
   And the cross from someone she has not met, well, not yet. *(To Chorus)*

4. *Repeat 2nd Verse*

SHELF IN THE ROOM

Words and Music by
TRAVIS MEEKS

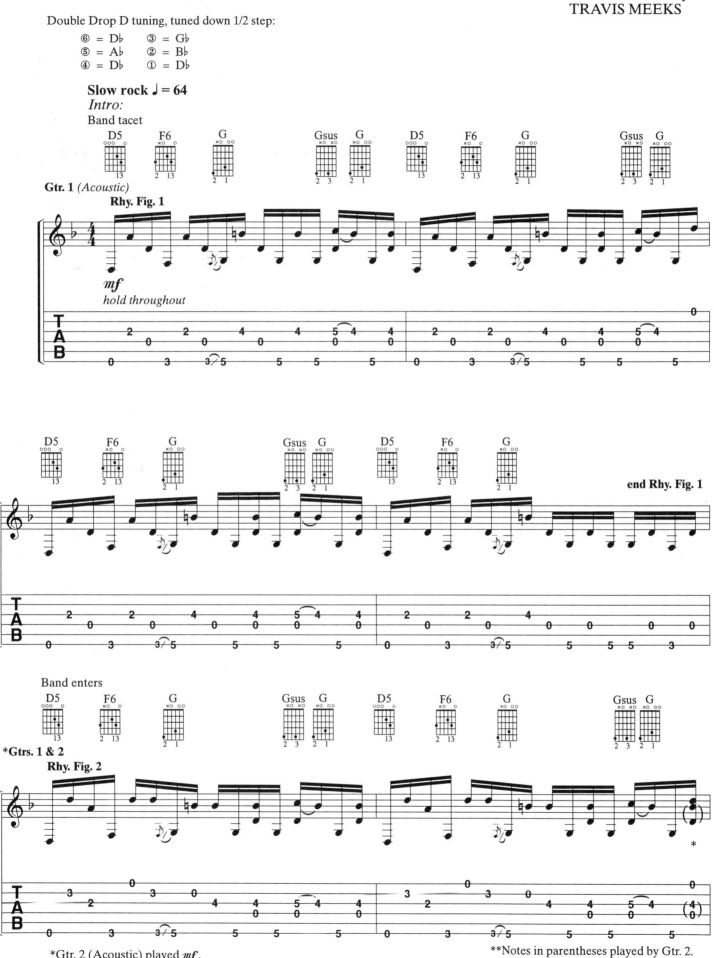

*Gtr. 2 (Acoustic) played *mf*.

**Notes in parentheses played by Gtr. 2.

Shelf in the Room - 9 - 1

Chorus:

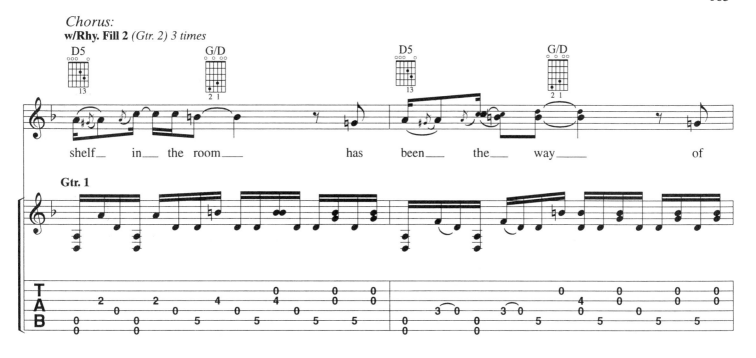

shelf___ in___ the room___   has been___ the___ way___ of

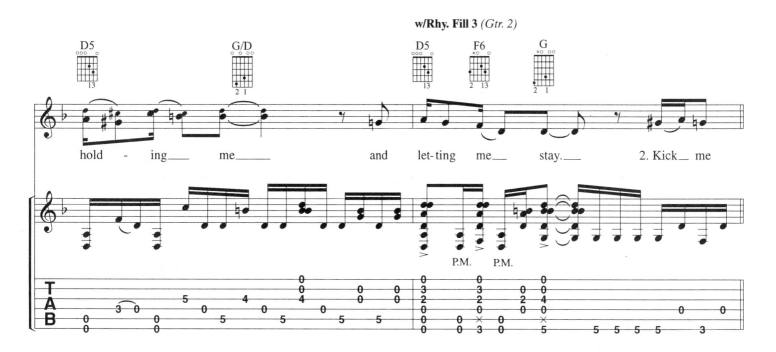

hold - ing___ me___   and let-ting me___ stay.___   2. Kick___ me

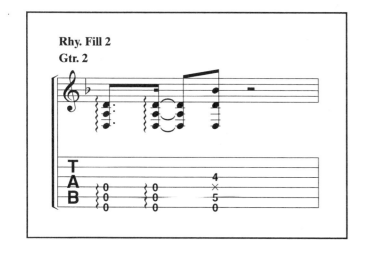

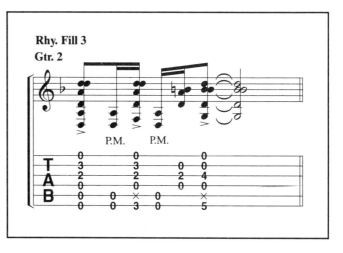

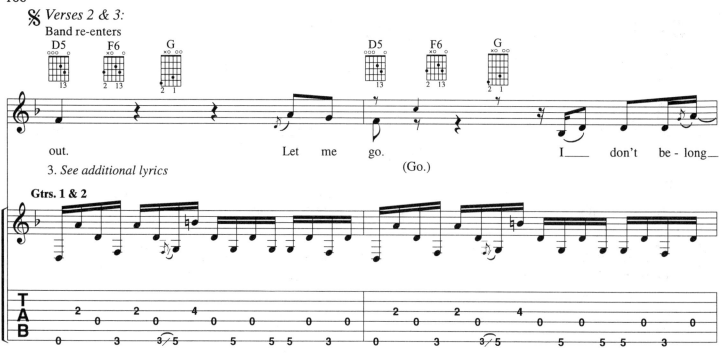

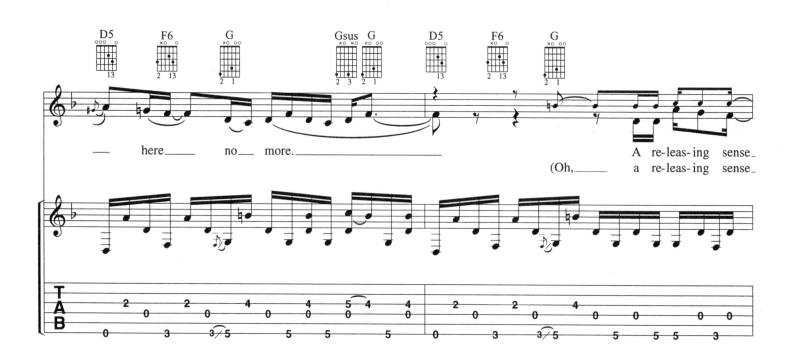

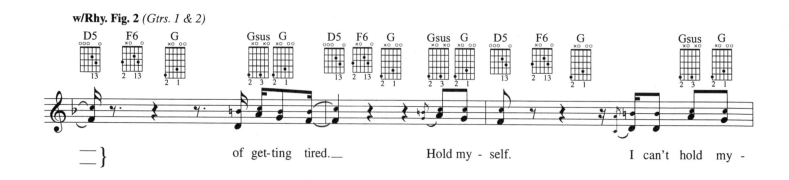

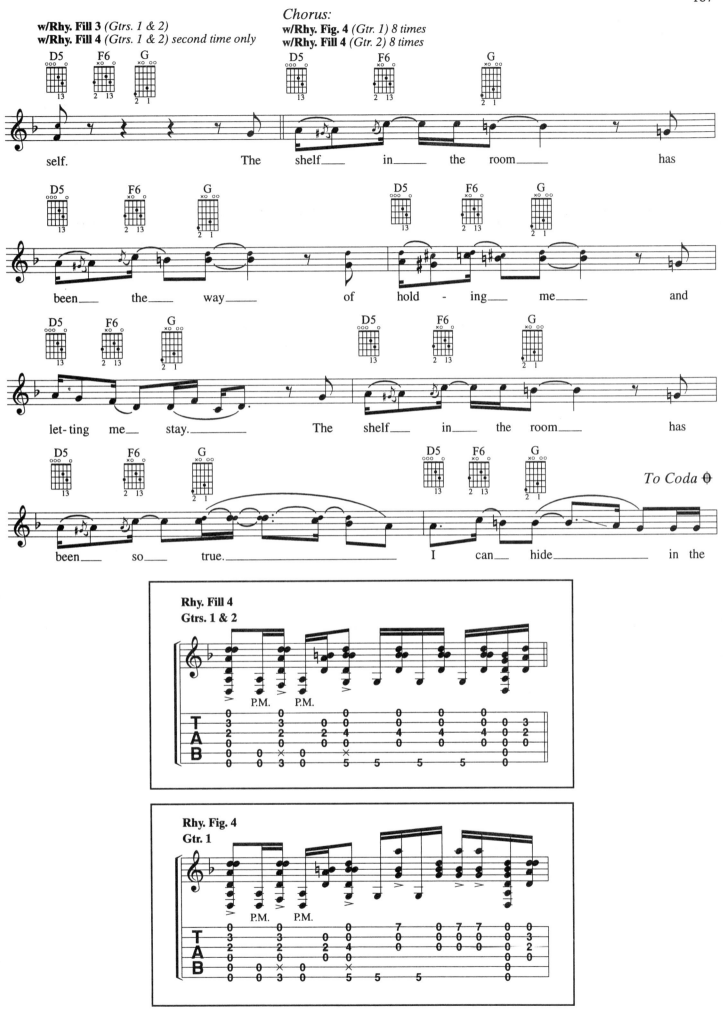

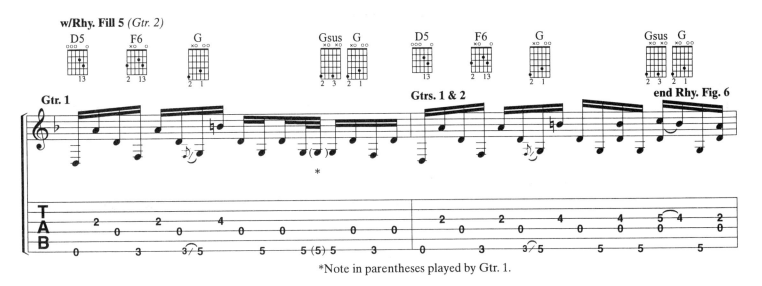

*Note in parentheses played by Gtr. 1.

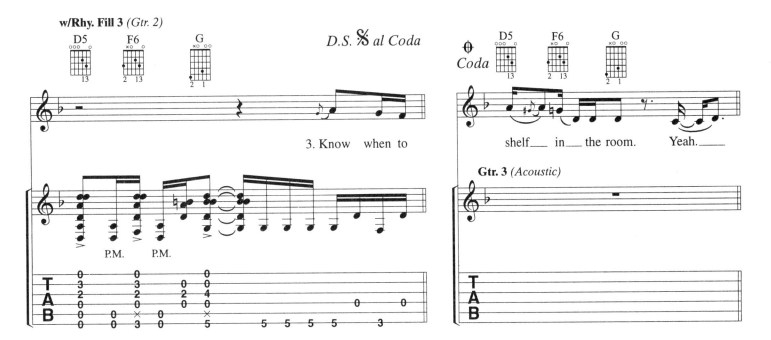

3. Know when to

shelf___ in___ the room.   Yeah.___

Verse 3:
Know when to listen.
Know what to listen for.
Believe in resistance,
Don't let them tell you anymore.
Is there anyway (No.)
To get away? (No.)
Ask myself,
While I stay inside.
(To Chorus:)

SHERRY FRASER

Words and Music by
JOHN WOZNIAK

Sherry Fraser – 2 – 1

Sherry Fraser – 2 – 2

SOMEONE ELSE'S SONG

Words and Music by
JEFF TWEEDY

Someone Else's Song – 5 – 1

𝄋 *Verse:*

1. Well, I can't tell you an - y - thing
2.3. *See additional lyrics*

Someone Else's Song – 5 – 4

Verse 2:
I keep on singing,
And your eyes, they just roll.
It sounds like someone else's song
From a long time ago.

Verse 3:
You already know the story,
And the chords are just the same.
You already know I love you,
Now I sound like what's-his-name.
But you can't stop me,
I want you to know.
I know it sounds like someone else's song
From a long time ago.
(To Coda)

MORNING SONG

Words and Music by
JEWEL KILCHER

*Capo at 1st fret.

Verse:

1. Let the phone ring. Let's go back to sleep.
2. See additional lyrics

Let the world spin out - side our door, you're the on - ly one that I want to see.

Tell your boss you're sick, hur - ry, get back in, I'm get - ting cold.

Morning Song - 4 - 1

Morning Song - 4 - 3

you_____ that I a - dore, I'm gon - na give you some more.
you_____ I'll be a poor man's wife, I'm gon - na give you some more.

Let the phone_ ring,_ let's go back to bed.

rit.

Verse 2:
We'll sit on the front porch,
The sun can warm my feet.
You can drink your coffee with sugar and cream,
I'll drink my decaf herbal tea.
Pretend we're perfect strangers
And that we never met.
My, how you remind me of a man I used to sleep with,
That's a face I'd never forget.
You can be Henry Miller and I'll be Anais Nin,
Except this time it'll be even better,
We'll stay together in the end.
Come on, darlin', let's go back to bed.
(To Chorus:)

STRONG ENOUGH

Words and Music by
SHERYL CROW, KEVIN GILBERT, BRIAN MACLEOD,
DAVID RICKETTS, BILL BOTTRELL, and DAVID BAERWALD

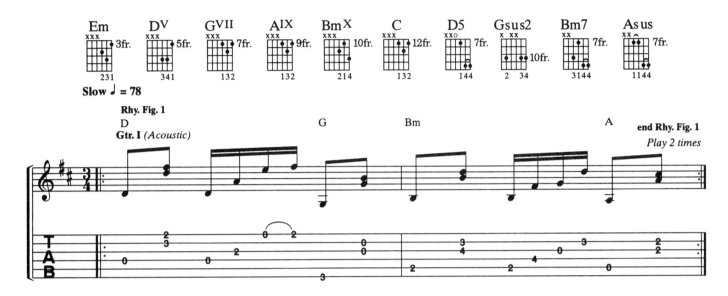

Slow ♩ = 78

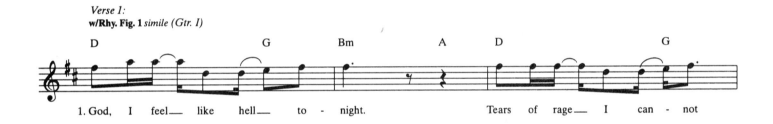

1. God, I feel like hell to-night. Tears of rage I can-not

fight I'd be the last to help you un-der-stand. Are you

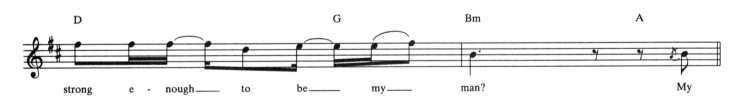

strong e-nough to be my man? My

Strong Enough - 3 - 1

Interlude 1:
w/Rhy. Fig 1 *simile (Gtr.I)*
w/Gtr. II *(12 string Acoustic), simile*

man.

Verses 2, 3 & 4:
w/Rhy. Fig. 1 *(Gtrs. I & II)*

1. Noth - ing's true___ and noth - ing's___ right. So let me be___ a - lone to -

2.3. See additional lyrics

night. 'Cause you can't change___ the way___ I am. Are you

To Coda I

strong e - nought___ to be___ my___ man?

Chorus:
Rhy. Fig. 2

Gtr. II

Lie_____ to me.___ I

Rhy. Fig. 3
Gtr. I

prom - ise,___ I'll be - lieve.___

end Rhy. Fig. 2

end Rhy. Fig. 3

Strong Enough - 3 - 2

Verse 3:
I have a face I cannot show.
I make the rules up as I go.
It's try and love me if you can.
Are you strong enough to be my man?
My man.

Verse 4:
When I've shown you that I just don't care,
When I'm throwing punches in the air,
When I'm broken down and I can't stand,
Will you be man enough to be my man?

Strong Enough - 3 - 3

SUNKEN TREASURE

Words and Music by
JEFF TWEEDY

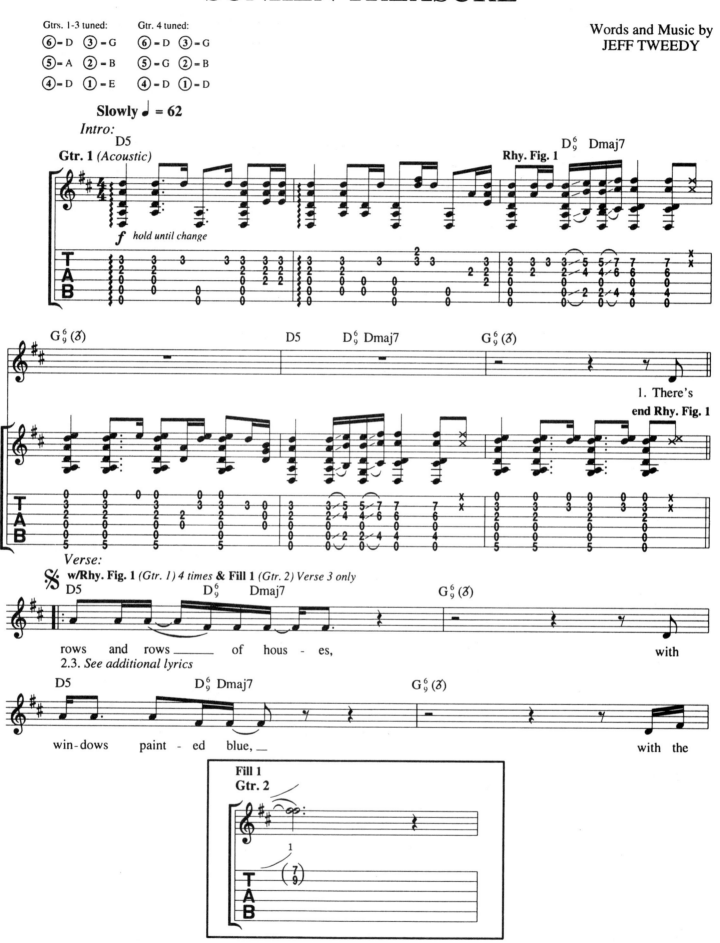

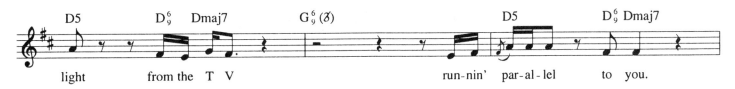

light   from the T V   run-nin' par-al-lel   to you.

But there is   no sunk - en treas-ure

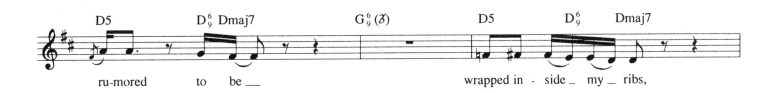

ru-mored   to be __   wrapped in - side __ my __ ribs,

To Coda

in   a sea   black __ with ink. __   I __ am

Chorus:

I __ am so __   out-ta tune   with you.

so ___   out of tune __   with you.

*Band plays different chords.

w/Rhy. Fig. 1 *(Gtr. 1)*

you.

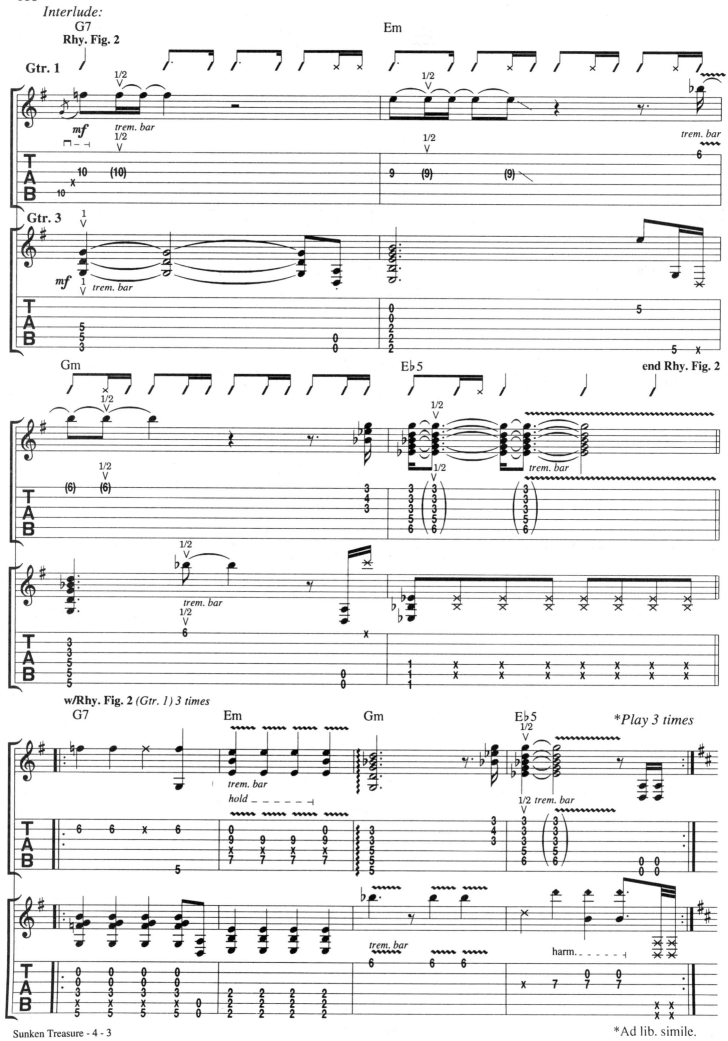

*Ad lib. simile.

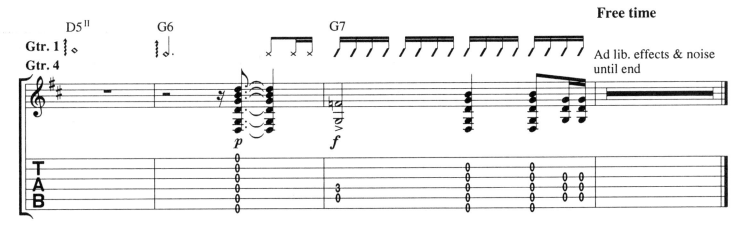

Verse 2:
If I had a mountain,
I'd try to fold it over.
If I had a boat,
You know I'd be traveling all over.
And I'd leave it on the shore,
And I'd leave it for somebody.
Surely there's somebody
Who needs it more than me.

Verse 3:
While all the leaves will burn
And autumn fire then return.
All the fires we burn
All will return.
Music is my savior.
And I was named by rock and roll.
I was named by rock and roll.
I was tamed by rock and roll.
I got my name from rock and roll.

SUNNY CAME HOME

Words and Music by
SHAWN COLVIN and JOHN LEVENTHAL

*Rhy. Fig. 1 is mandolin arr. for Acoustic gtr.

Sunny Came Home - 9 - 1

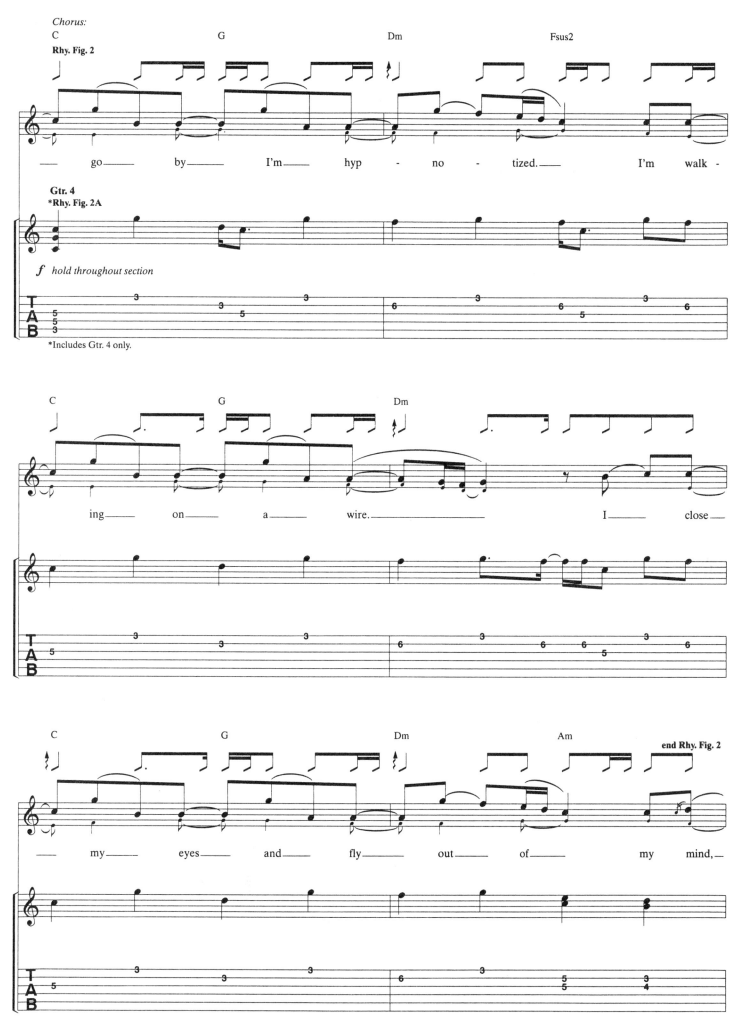

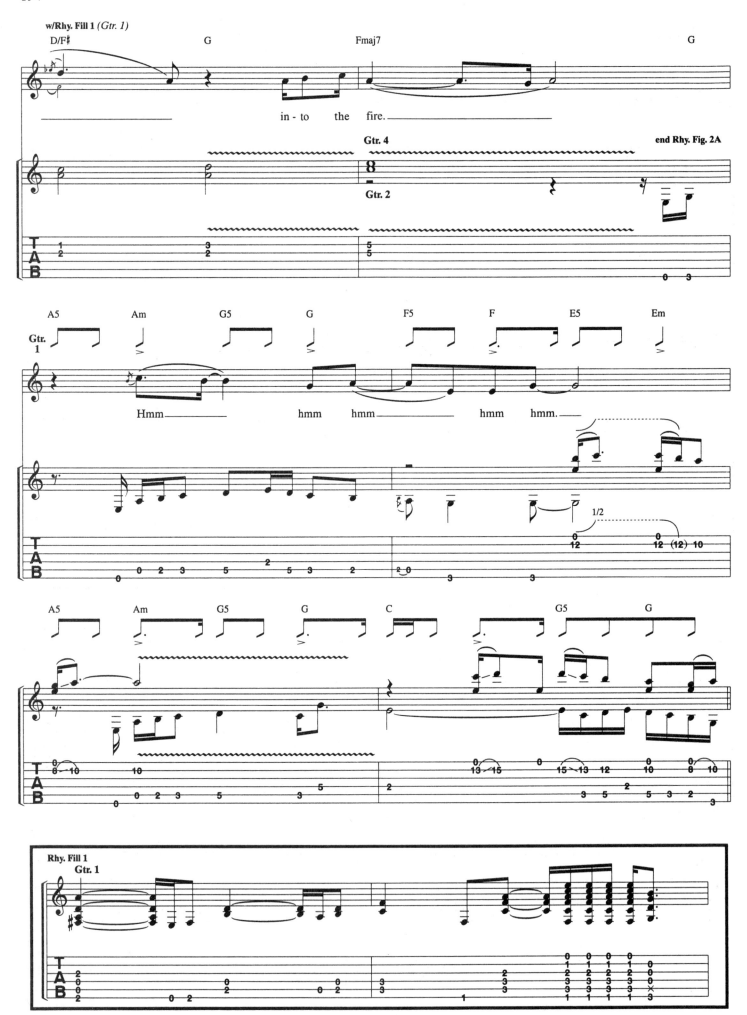

Sunny Came Home - 9 - 8

TEARS IN HEAVEN

Words and Music by
WILL JENNINGS and ERIC CLAPTON

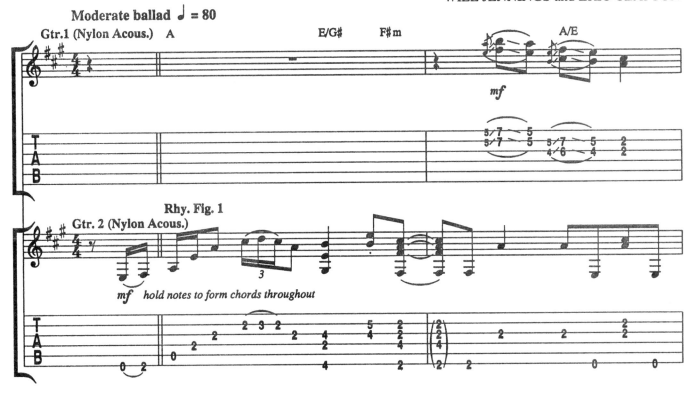

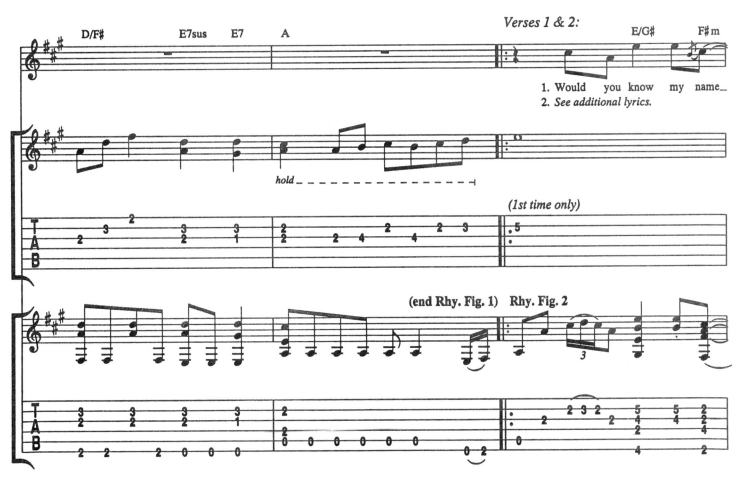

Tears in Heaven - 3 - 1

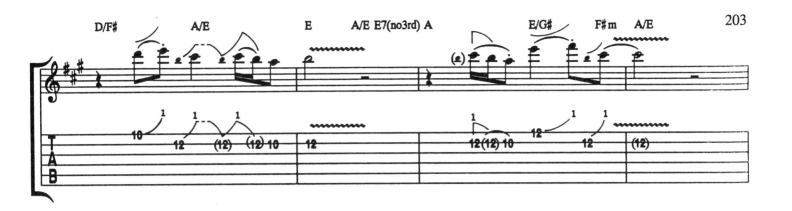

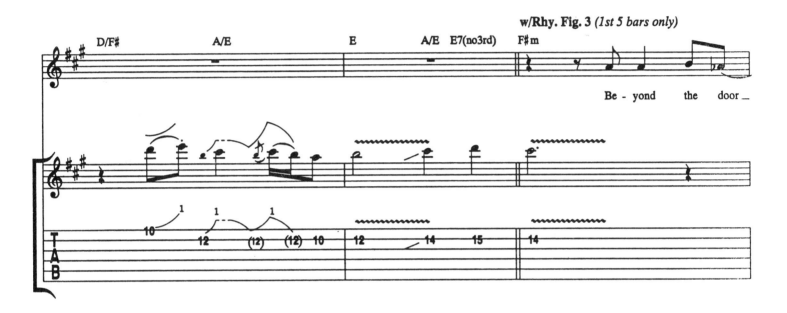

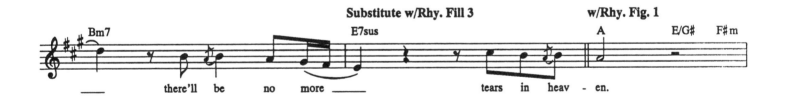

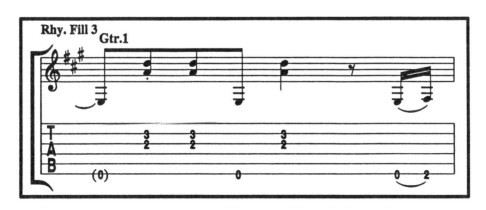

Verse 3:
w/Rhy. Fill 2 & Fill 4　　　　　　　　**w/Rhy. Fig. 2** *(bars 2-8)*

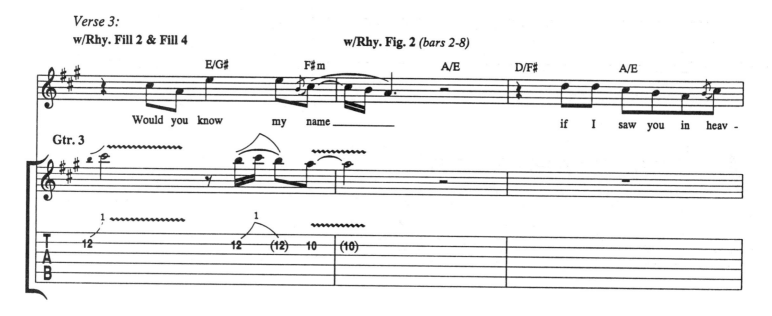

Would you know　my　name _____　if I saw you in heav-

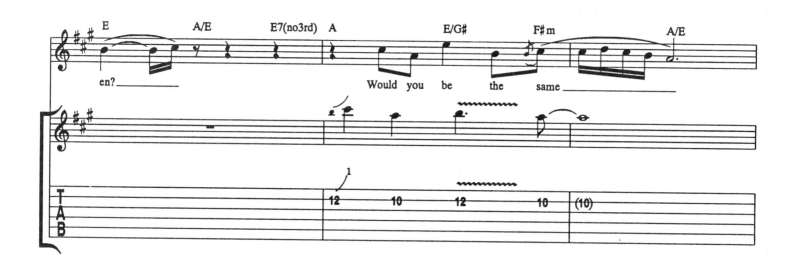

-en? _____　Would you be the same _____

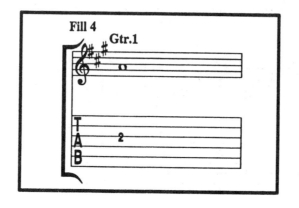

Tears in Heaven - 8 - 7

Verse 2:
Would you hold my hand
If I saw you in heaven?
Would you help me stand
If I saw you in heaven?
I'll find my way,
Through night and day,
'Cause I know I just can't stay
Here in heaven.

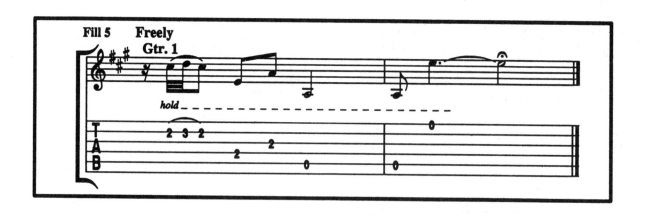

THREE MARLENAS

Words and Music by
JAKOB DYLAN

**Chord symbols in parentheses are concert pitch for Gtr. 2.
Chord symbols without parentheses are transposed for gtr. and vocal.

Verse 2:
Now, lookin' out across the city lights,
She thought they'd be a good pair.
Well, he could make a livin' sellin' cars,
Maybe she could work there.
She's gonna pick a star in the night
And pray to make it all right.
She tried so hard not to pick a kite.
She always prayed to headlights.
(To Chorus:)

Verse 3:
Man, I think I'm gonna buy myself a Rolls,
Maybe a Chevrolet.
One where I can pull that top down,
Just let my radio play.
Now, I'm headin' out on that highway.
I'm goin' right out of state.
Now, I ain't lookin' back until I'm gone,
Right through heaven's gate.
(To Chorus:)

TIL I HEAR IT FROM YOU

Words and Music by
JESSE VALENZUELA, ROBIN WILSON
and MARSHALL CRENSHAW

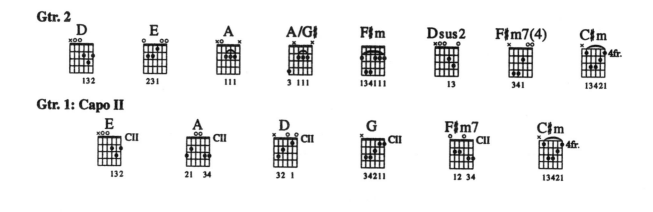

*Gtr. 1 w/capo at 2nd fret. TAB numbers indicate actual fret numbers with 2 thought of as open;
Gtr. 1 is two gtrs. arr. for one (throughout).

Til I Hear It From You - 8 - 1

*Sing harmony 2nd time only.

Til I Hear It From You - 8 - 2

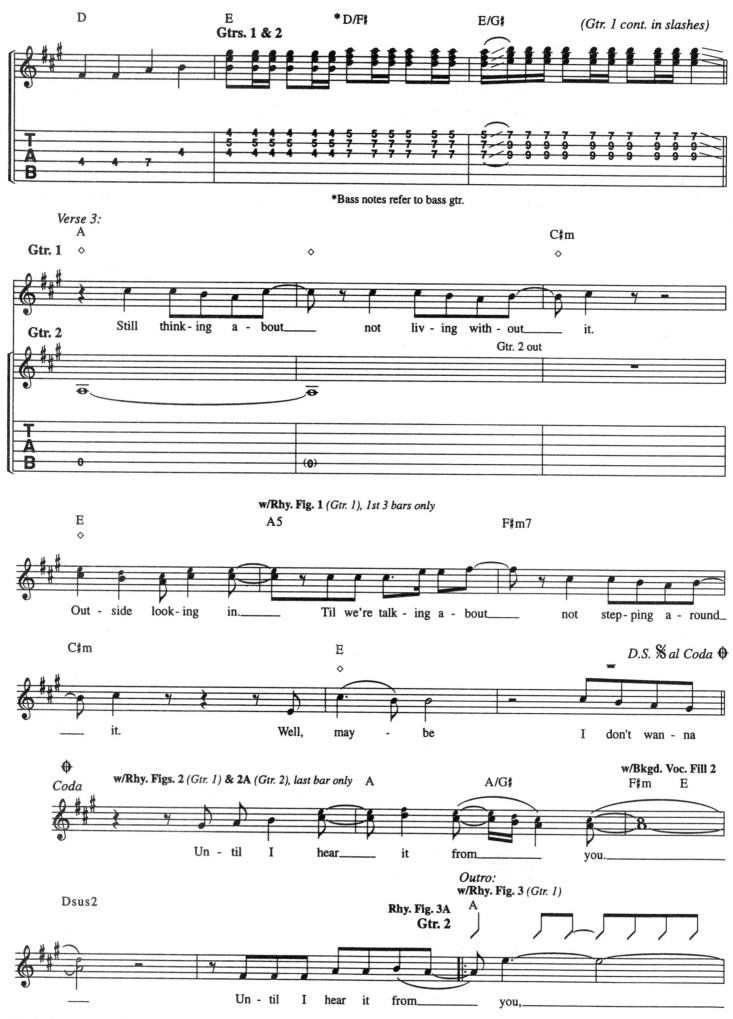

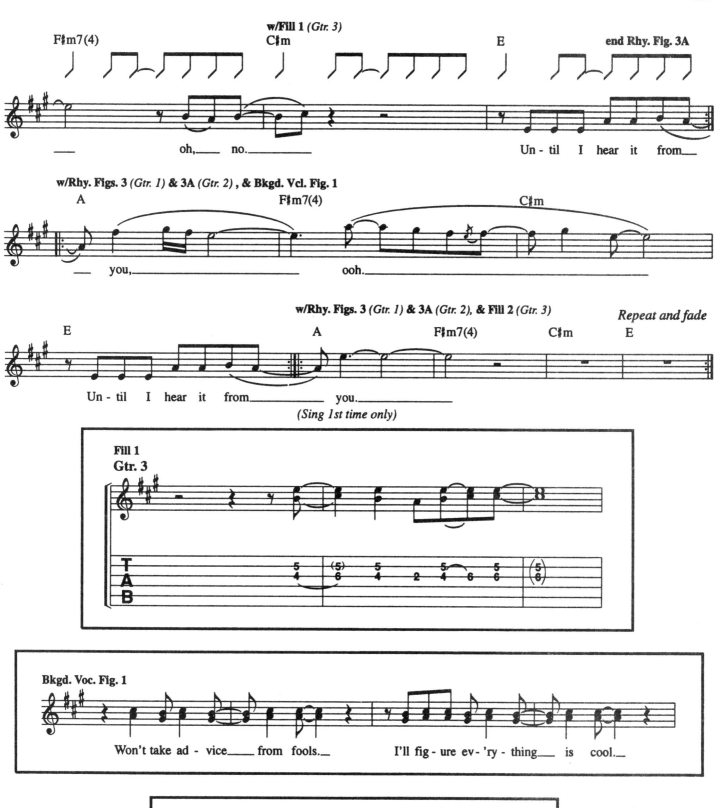

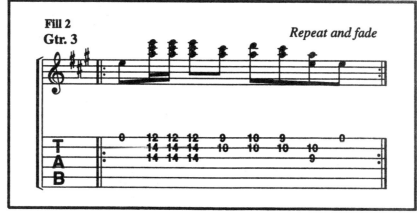

TOUCH, PEEL AND STAND

Words and Music by
TRAVIS MEEKS

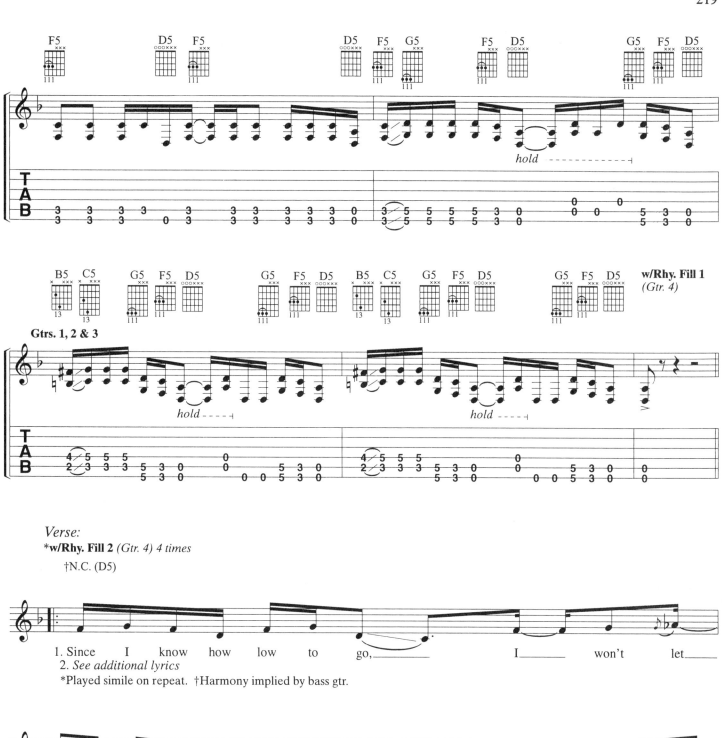

Verse:
*w/Rhy. Fill 2 *(Gtr. 4) 4 times*

†N.C. (D5)

1. Since I know how low to go,_____ I___ won't let____
2. *See additional lyrics*
*Played simile on repeat. †Harmony implied by bass gtr.

___ it show.__ Won't__ you touch__ me, touch me? I___ won't let__

Rhy. Fill 1
Gtr. 4 *(Acoustic)*

Rhy. Fill 2
Gtr. 4

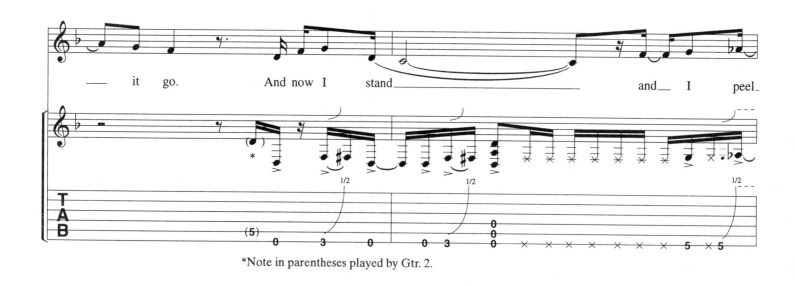

— it go.   And now I   stand_____   and_ I   peel_

*Note in parentheses played by Gtr. 2.

— for__ more.__   Won't_ you   touch__ me,   touch   me?_____   I__won't

hold bend

Chorus:
w/Rhy. Fig. 1 *(Gtrs. 1, 2 & 3) 2 times*

let   it   go.___   Yes, I   fi-   n'lly   found   a   rea-   son,   I___   don't

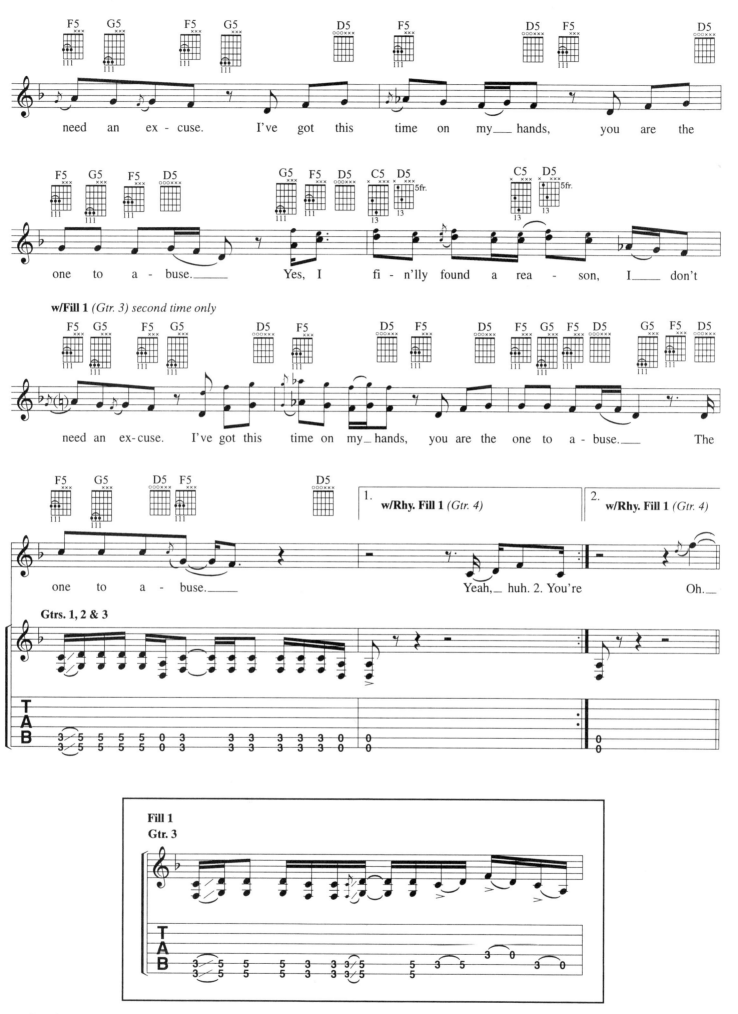

222

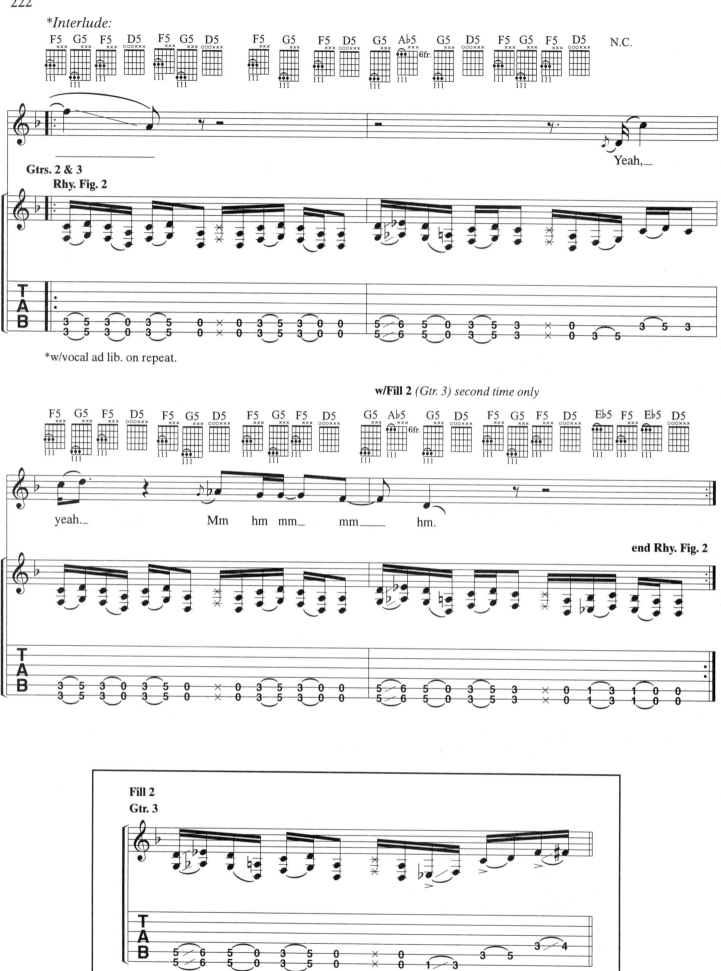

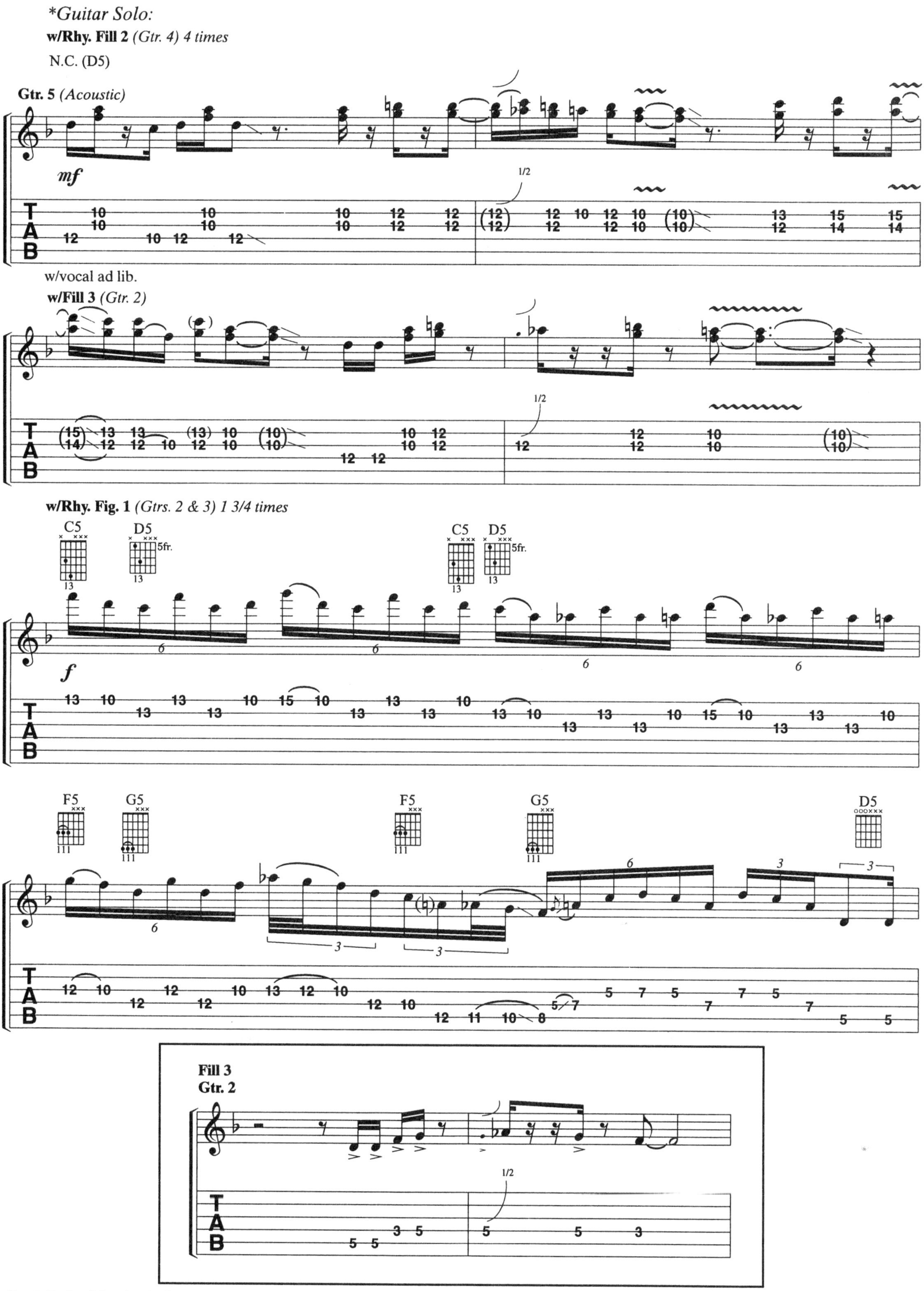

Guitar Solo:

w/Rhy. Fill 2 *(Gtr. 4) 4 times*

N.C. (D5)

Gtr. 5 *(Acoustic)*

mf

w/vocal ad lib.

w/Fill 3 *(Gtr. 2)*

w/Rhy. Fig. 1 *(Gtrs. 2 & 3) 1 3/4 times*

Fill 3
Gtr. 2

Touch, Peel and Stand - 11 - 6

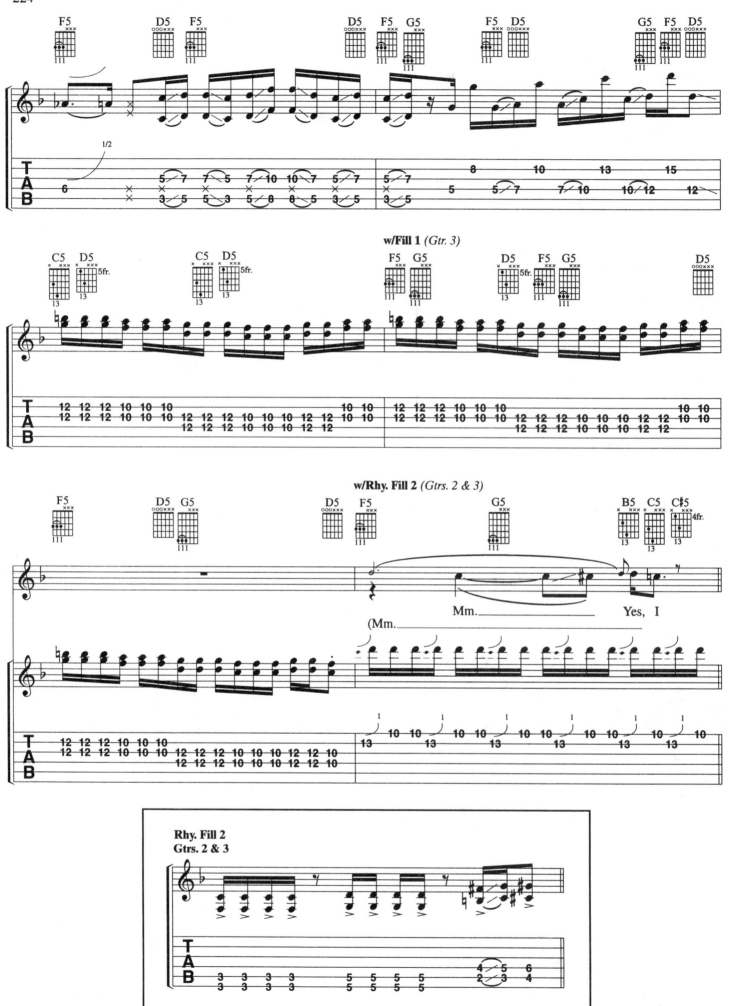

Chorus:

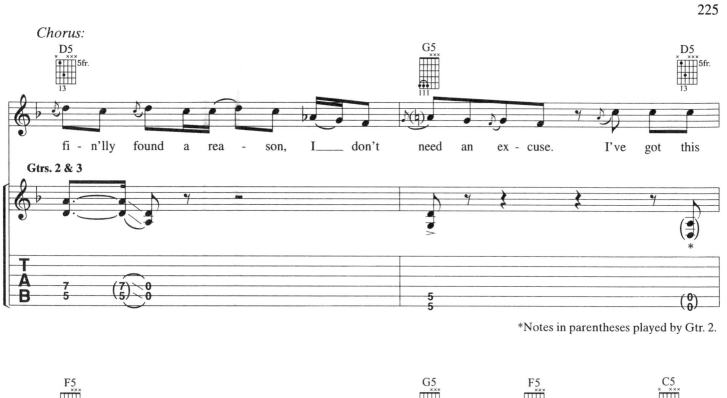

fi - n'lly found a rea - son, I___ don't need an ex - cuse. I've got this

Gtrs. 2 & 3

*Notes in parentheses played by Gtr. 2.

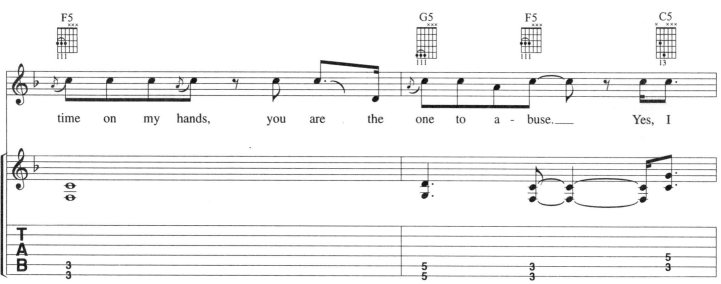

time on my hands, you are the one to a - buse.___ Yes, I

w/Rhy. Fig. 1 *(Gtrs. 1, 2 & 3) 4 times*

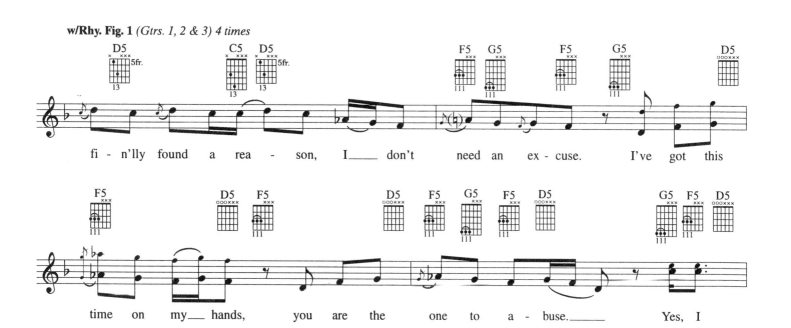

fi - n'lly found a rea - son, I___ don't need an ex - cuse. I've got this

time on my___ hands, you are the one to a - buse._____ Yes, I

Outro:
w/Rhy. Fig. 2 *(Gtrs. 2 & 3)*

Oh.____

*w/vocal ad lib. on repeats.

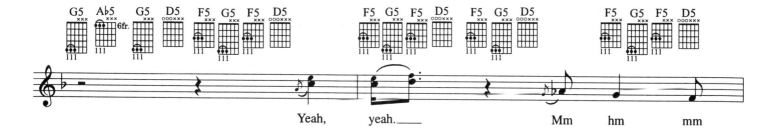

Yeah, yeah.____ Mm hm mm

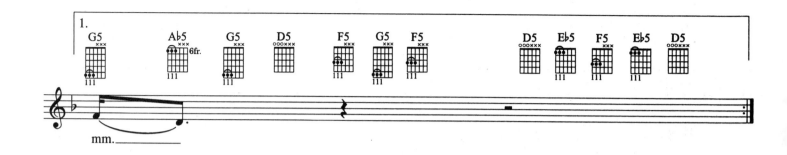

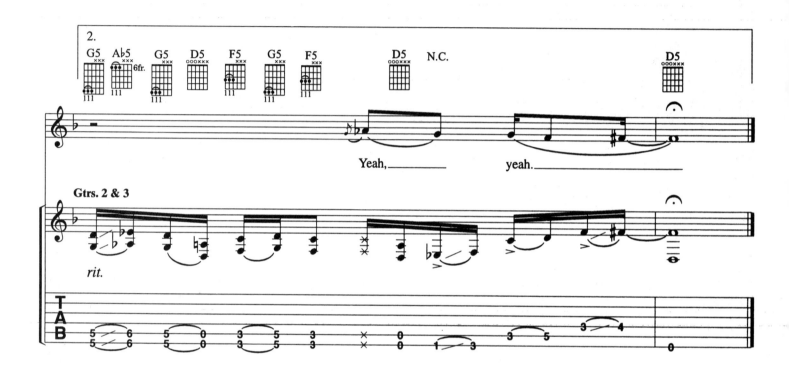

Verse 2:
You're always talking back to me.
You won't let it be.
Won't you touch me, touch me?
It never bothered you before.
Now I stand and I peel for more.
Won't you youch me, touch me?
I won't let it go.
(To Chorus:)

WHO WILL SAVE YOUR SOUL

Words and Music by
JEWEL KILCHER

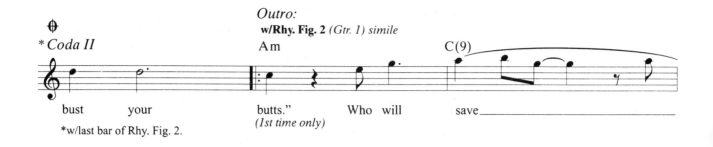

*Coda II

*w/last bar of Rhy. Fig. 2.

bust your butts." Who will save

Outro:
w/Rhy. Fig. 2 (Gtr. 1) simile

Am

(1st time only)

C(9)

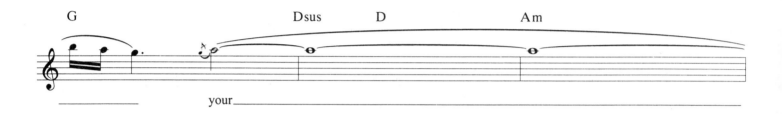

G

your

Dsus   D   Am

C(9)   G   Dsus   *Repeat and fade   D

soul

*Lead vocal ad lib on repeats.

Verse 3:
Some are walking, some are talking, some are stalking their kill.
Got social security, but that don't pay your bills.
There are addictions to feed and there are mouths to pay,
So you bargain with the devil, but you're O. K. for today.
Say that you love them, take their money and run.
Say, "It's been swell, sweetheart, but it was just one of those things,
Those flings, those strings you got to cut,
So get out on the streets, girls, and bust your butts."
(To Chorus:)

THE WORLD I KNOW

Music by ED ROLAND & ROSS CHILDRESS
Lyrics by ED ROLAND

The World I Know - 5 - 1

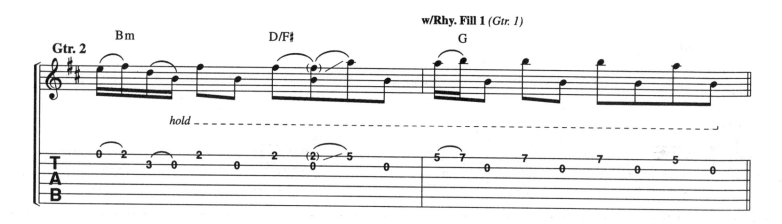

Pre-Chorus:
w/Rhy. Figs. **2** (Gtr. 1, simile) & **2A** (Gtr. 2)

I drink my-self of new found pit-y sit-ting a-lone in New York Cit-y and I

don't know why, don't know why. So I walk *up* on high

and I step to the edge to see my world be-low.

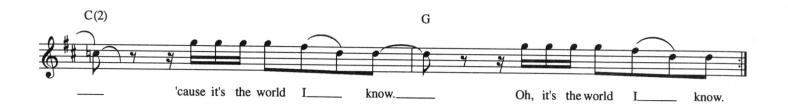

And I laugh *at* my-self while the tears roll down

'cause it's the world I know. Oh, it's the world I know.

Outro:

Gtr. 1

Gtr. 2

Verse 2:
Are we listening to hymns of offering?
Have we eyes to see that love is gathering?

Pre-Chorus:
All the words that I've been reading
Have now started the act of bleeding
Into one, into one.
(To Chorus:)

YOU AND THE MONA LISA

Words and Music by
SHAWN COLVIN and JOHN LEVENTHAL

You and the Mona Lisa - 6 - 1

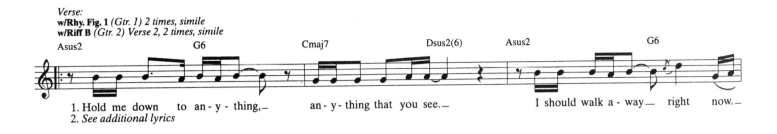

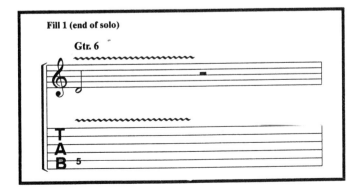

You and the Mona Lisa - 6 - 2

Oh, I

Noth-ing in par-tic-u-lar,— just you and the Mo-na Li-sa.

You and the Mona Lisa - 6 - 4

Noth - ing   in   par - tic - u - lar,___ just   you   and   the   Mo - na   Li -   sa.

Verse 2:
Nothing in particular and everything in between.
This is what you mean to me.
Only you and only me, climbing in the right direction,
On the way to everything.

Chorus 2:
We were walking up high,
And no one thought to try,
But I was the one to blame.
And it was just a mirage,
So I hid in the garage
'Til somebody called your name.
(Guitar Solo:)

YOU CAN SLEEP WHILE I DRIVE

Lyrics and Music by
MELISSA ETHERIDGE

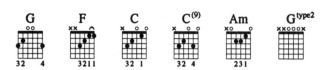

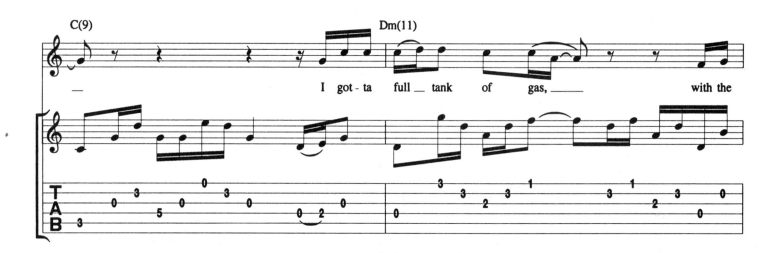

You Can Sleep While I Drive – 6 – 1

You Can Sleep While I Drive – 6 – 2

Gtr. 1 *cont. in notation*

ten - tions are true, __ won't you take me __ with you. __ And

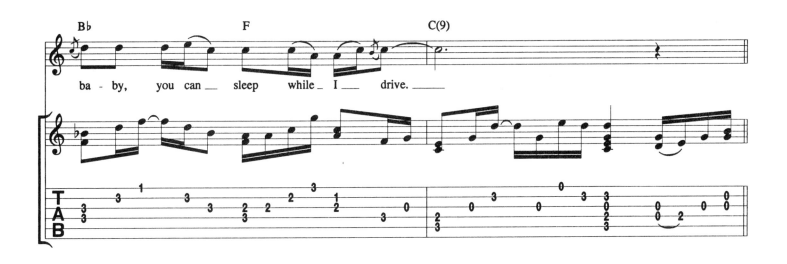

ba - by, you can __ sleep while __ I drive. __

Interlude:

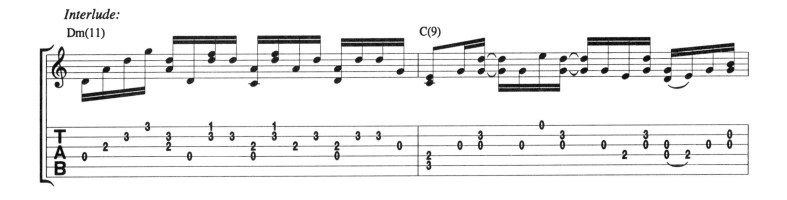

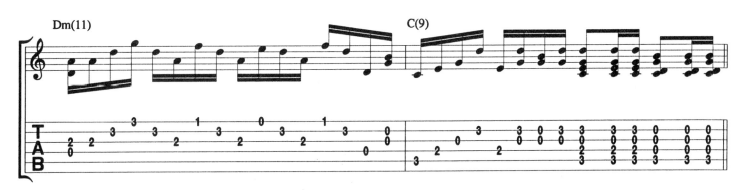

Bridge II:

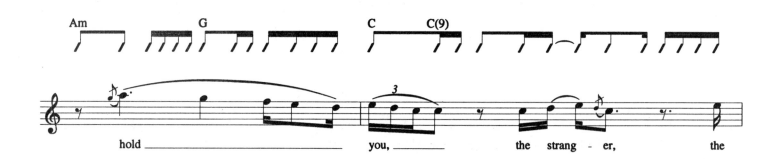

Oh, _____ Oh, Oh, _____ is it oth - er arms _____ you _____ want _____ to

hold _____ you, _____ the strang - er, the

lov - er, you're _____ free. _____ Can't you get that with me? _____ 4. Come on

*Bass gtr. plays D.

Verse 4:
a tempo

ba - by, let's get out of _____ this town. _____ I got a

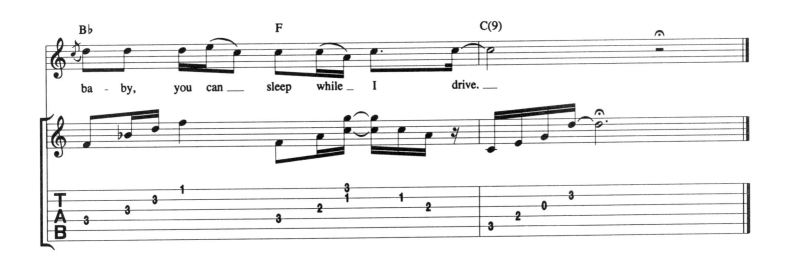

Verse 3:
We'll go through Tucson up to Santa Fe.
And Barbara in Nashville says we're welcome to stay.
I'll buy you glasses in Texas, a hat from New Orleans.
And in the morning you can tell me your dreams.
(To Bridge I:)

You Can Sleep While I Drive – 6 – 6

YOU WERE MEANT FOR ME

Words and Music by
JEWEL KILCHER and STEVE POLZ

All gtrs. tune down 1/2 step:

⑥ = E♭ ③ = G♭

⑤ = A♭ ② = B♭

④ = D♭ ① = E♭

Moderately ♩ = 132

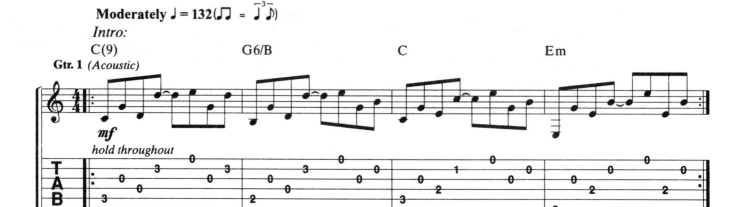

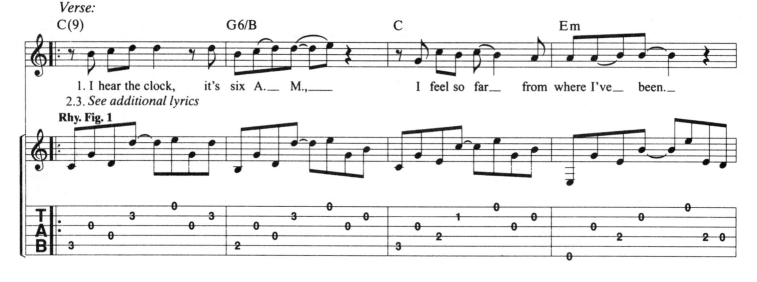

You Were Meant for Me - 4 - 1

You Were Meant for Me - 4 - 2

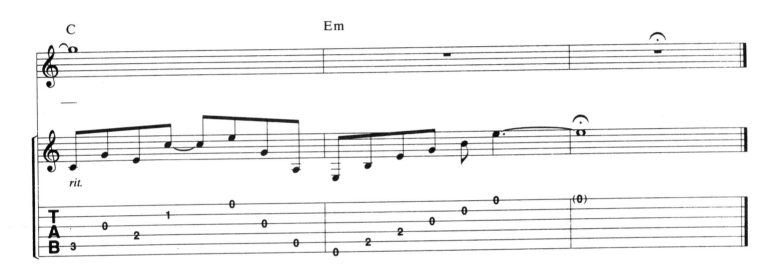

Verse 2:
I called my mama, she was out for a walk.
Consoled a cup of coffee, but it didn't wanna talk.
So I picked up a paper, it was more bad news.
More hearts being broken or people being used.
Put on my coat in the pouring rain.
I saw a movie, it just wasn't the same.
'Cause it was happy and I was sad
And it made me miss you, oh, so bad.
(To Chorus:)

Verse 3:
I brush my teeth and put the cap back on.
I know you hate it when I leave the light on.
I pick a book up and then I turn the sheets down,
And then I take a deep breath and a good look around.
Put on my pj's and hop into bed.
I'm half alive, but I feel mostly dead.
I try and tell myself it'll be all right,
I just shouldn't think anymore tonight.
(To Chorus:)

GUITAR TAB GLOSSARY **

TABLATURE EXPLANATION

READING TABLATURE: Tablature illustrates the six strings of the guitar. Notes and chords are indicated by the placement of fret numbers on a given string(s).

String ⑥, 3rd Fret   String ① 12th Fret   A "C" Chord   C Chord Arpeggiated
String ③ 13th Fret

BENDING NOTES

HALF STEP: Play the note and bend string one half step.*

WHOLE STEP: Play the note and bend string one whole step.

WHOLE STEP AND A HALF: Play the note and bend string a whole step and a half.

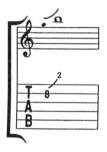

TWO STEPS: Play the note and bend string two whole steps.

SLIGHT BEND (Microtone): Play the note and bend string slightly to the equivalent of half a fret.

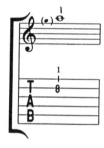

PREBEND (Ghost Bend): Bend to the specified note, before the string is picked.

PREBEND AND RELEASE: Bend the string, play it, then release to the original note.

REVERSE BEND: Play the already-bent string, then immediately drop it down to the fretted note.

BEND AND RELEASE: Play the note and gradually bend to the next pitch, then release to the original note. Only the first note is attacked.

BENDS INVOLVING MORE THAN ONE STRING: Play the note and bend string while playing an additional note (or notes) on another string(s). Upon release, relieve pressure from additional note(s), causing original note to sound alone.

BENDS INVOLVING STATIONARY NOTES: Play notes and bend lower pitch, then hold until release begins (indicated at the point where line becomes solid).

UNISON BEND: Play both notes and immediately bend the lower note to the same pitch as the higher note.

DOUBLE NOTE BEND: Play both notes and immediately bend both strings simultaneously.

*A half step is the smallest interval in Western music; it is equal to one fret. A whole step equals two frets.

© 1990 Beam Me Up Music
c/o CPP/Belwin, Inc. Miami, Florida 33014
International Copyright Secured   Made in U.S.A.   All Rights Reserved   **By Kenn Chipkin and Aaron Stang

RHYTHM SLASHES

STRUM INDICA-TIONS: Strum with indicated rhythm.

The chord voicings are found on the first page of the transcription underneath the song title.

INDICATING SINGLE NOTES USING RHYTHM SLASHES: Very often single notes are incorporated into a rhythm part. The note name is indicated above the rhythm slash with a fret number and a string indication.

ARTICULATIONS

HAMMER ON: Play lower note, then "hammer on" to higher note with another finger. Only the first note is attacked.

LEFT HAND HAMMER: Hammer on the first note played on each string with the left hand.

PULL OFF: Play higher note, then "pull off" to lower note with another finger. Only the first note is attacked.

FRET-BOARD TAPPING: "Tap" onto the note indicated by + with a finger of the pick hand, then pull off to the following note held by the fret hand.

TAP SLIDE: Same as fretboard tapping, but the tapped note is slid randomly up the fretboard, then pulled off to the following note.

BEND AND TAP TECHNIQUE: Play note and bend to specified interval. While holding bend, tap onto note indicated.

LEGATO SLIDE: Play note and slide to the following note. (Only first note is attacked).

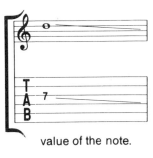

LONG GLISSAN-DO: Play note and slide in specified direction for the full value of the note.

SHORT GLISSAN-DO: Play note for its full value and slide in specified direction at the last possible moment.

PICK SLIDE: Slide the edge of the pick in specified direction across the length of the string(s).

MUTED STRINGS: A percussive sound is made by laying the fret hand across all six strings while pick hand strikes specified area (low, mid, high strings).

PALM MUTE: The note or notes are muted by the palm of the pick hand by lightly touching the string(s) near the bridge.

TREMOLO PICKING: The note or notes are picked as fast as possible.

TRILL: Hammer on and pull off consecutively and as fast as possible between the original note and the grace note.

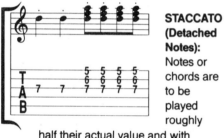

ACCENT: Notes or chords are to be played with added emphasis.

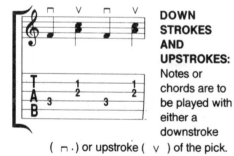

STACCATO (Detached Notes): Notes or chords are to be played roughly half their actual value and with separation.

DOWN STROKES AND UPSTROKES: Notes or chords are to be played with either a downstroke (⊓) or upstroke (∨) of the pick.

VIBRATO: The pitch of a note is varied by a rapid shaking of the fret hand finger, wrist, and forearm.

HARMONICS

NATURAL HARMONIC: A finger of the fret hand lightly touches the note or notes indicated in the tab and is played by the pick hand.

ARTIFICIAL HARMONIC: The first tab number is fretted, then the pick hand produces the harmonic by using a finger to lightly touch the same string at the second tab number (in parenthesis) and is then picked by another finger.

ARTIFICIAL "PINCH" HAR-MONIC: A note is fretted as indicated by the tab, then the pick hand produces the harmonic by squeezing the pick firmly while using the tip of the index finger in the pick attack. If parenthesis are found around the fretted note, it does not sound. No parenthesis means both the fretted note and A.H. are heard simultaneously.

TREMOLO BAR

SPECIFIED INTERVAL: The pitch of a note or chord is lowered to a specified interval and then may or may not return to the original pitch. The activity of the tremolo bar is graphically represented by peaks and valleys.

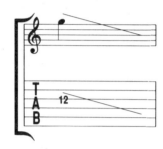

UN-SPECIFIED INTERVAL: The pitch of a note or a chord is lowered to an unspecified interval.